KIZILKAR

D1593882

By George Robert Elford and published by
New English Library

DEVIL'S GUARD
KIZILKAR

KIZILKAR
RED SNOW
George Robert Elford

NEW ENGLISH LIBRARY

A New English Library Original Publication, 1984

Copyright © 1984 by George Robert Elford

All rights reserved. No part of this publication may be reproduced
or transmitted, in any form or by any means, without permission of
the publishers.

First NEL Paperback Edition June 1984

Conditions of sale: This book is sold subject
to the condition that it shall not, by way of
trade or otherwise, be lent, resold, hired out,
or otherwise circulated without the publisher's
prior consent in any form of binding or cover
other than that in which it is published and
without a similar condition including this
condition being imposed on the subsequent purchaser.

NEL Books are published by
New English Library,
Mill Road, Dunton Green,
Sevenoaks, Kent.
Editorial office: 47 Bedford Square, London WC1B 3DP

Made and printed in Great Britain by Richard Clay
(The Chaucer Press) Ltd, Bungay, Suffolk

Typeset in Times by Fleet Graphics, Enfield, Middlesex

Elford, George
  Kizilkar
  1. Afghanistan—History—Intervention—1979
  I. Title
  958.1'04   DA592

  ISBN 0 450 05692 9

For my dear Italian friends,
Marcello Puccetti, Giacomo
Rinaldi, Domenico de Luca and
the Agostini family, IL SERGENTE,
Monte di Fo. With special thanks
to the officers of the Vigili
Urbani of Galluzzo and Impruneta.

George Robert Elford
Florence 1982/83

CONTENTS

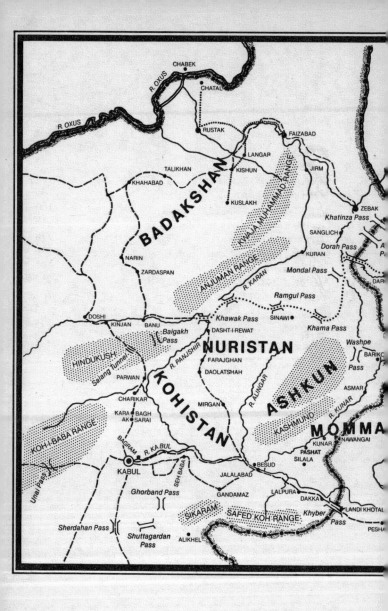

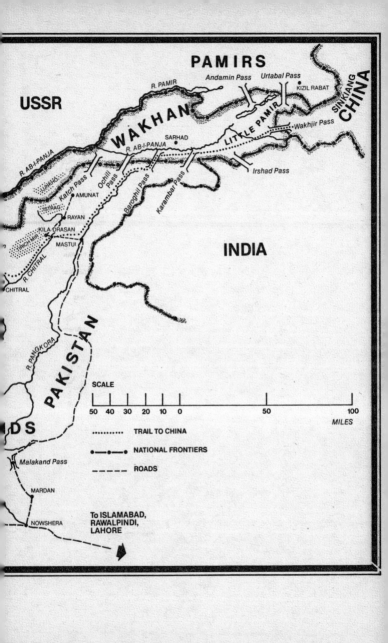

PAMIRS

USSR

R. PAMIR
Andamin Pass   *Urtabal Pass*   KIZIL RABAT

SINKIANG

CHINA

WAKHAN   SARHAD   LITTLE PAMIR   Wakhjir Pass

R. AB-I-PANJA   R. AB-I-PANJA

R. AB-I-PANJA

LUNKHO   Katch Pass   Ochili Pass   Baroghil Pass   Irshad Pass

AMUNAT   Karambar Pass

ISTRAG   RAYAN

KILA DRASAN   **INDIA**

TIRICH MIR   MASTUJ

R. CHITRAL

CHITRAL

PAKISTAN

R. PANGKORA

SCALE

50 40 30 20 10 0   50   100

MILES

DS

.... TRAIL TO CHINA

•—•—•—• NATIONAL FRONTIERS

— — — ROADS

Malakand Pass

MARDAN

NOWSHERA

To ISLAMABAD,
RAWALPINDI,
LAHORE

KIZILKAR
—Red Snow—

A story from fighting Afghanistan

FOREWORD

Fourteen months after the Soviet invasion of Afghanistan, Ali Ghazi Khan, thirty-seven, a former teacher in Jalalabad and leader of some three hundred resolute *mojahedins* of the Anjuman range, told me:

'The free world has already forgotten us. The front-page reports have disappeared from the newspapers. Afghan resistance to Russian vandalism is now given a few, insignificant lines in the back pages. As always, when facing Communist outrages, the United Nations fell silent and has given Moscow its tacit consent to crush us at leisure.

The friendly governments give us a few words of praise and encouragement, then preoccupy themselves with other, to them more important world affairs. We are a remote and insignificant nation of a few million people, wild and backward and without any important natural resource. Striving for a homeland, the Palestinians receive daily attention, while the people of Afghanistan, whose centuries-old homeland has been seized by a foreign invader, are ignored. But of course, behind the Palestinians looms the important factor of Arab oil and Israel is not the USSR. Sometimes I wonder what the situation would be like if Israel had invaded Afghanistan and the Russians were in Palestine. Our country would be in the headlines and the Palestinian question would be buried under a mountain of silence, smothered by Soviet power and aggression.

The men in the Kremlin know from experience that if they ignore the initial uproar and persevere, the voices of protest will thin out, and the free world eventually bow before the brutal force. It has always been and will always be so. The free world has neither unity and solid principles, nor a consistent foreign policy. The great democracies have become complacent in their wealth and comfort; they have too much

13

to lose in a commercial or military confrontation with Communism and consequently try to hang on to what they have as long as possible, if only to slow down the process of losing. The Russians want to conquer the world – preferably without a global war, inch by inch, through subversion, causing tiny shocks but no great quakes.

Despite our backwardness we are not fools. We can face reality with pride and resolution. We neither beg for sympathy, nor do we expect any serious help from our reluctant friends. We are fighting for survival and will never compromise on the issue of our freedom. If the infidel invaders destroy our homes, we will continue fighting them in the mountains, in the ravines. We have already learned to survive on what the hills provide. The Russians may occupy Afghanistan for a hundred years, but our sons and grandsons will still fight them, and invaders will die every single day of those years.

The Afghans are like a good blade that can be bent but not broken. Our weapons are scarce, but not our faith in Allah and Islam. And is there a better weapon than faith?

If the godless enemy wants to stop us, Moscow will have to station a regiment in every village, on every hill, a tank at every hundred yards along every road and trail. But even then the Russians' peace of mind would be short-lived: we would reduce their regiments to battalions and the battalions to companies. We will turn Afghanistan into a huge graveyard for the invaders. We will never stop fighting them.'

Let this book be a modest reminder to the free world, commemorating the resolute struggle of a handful of brave men against a mighty superpower; only a few pages taken from the great book of Afghan history of scores of similar, still unwritten, or already forgotten stories born of fire and blood.

Nothing has been altered except their names.

THE BAZOOKA

FOURTEEN-YEAR-OLD Zahor Reza and his friend Muharrem Zarag, a year younger, had survived the Russian strike because they were high in the mountains, grazing the community flock of sixty sheep and goats. They were six miles from the Khawak Pass when the helicopter gunships raided their hamlet, thirty stone houses east of Banu.

Eight copters, manned by the 'friends of the Afghan people' came flying low over the valley of the Panjshir river, keeping out of sight, giving the inhabitants no chance to save themselves. They rose from the sheltered depression only in the last few miles, lifted over the plateau and opened fire with everything they had: bombs, rockets and machine guns. The raid lasted for only eight minutes; afterwards, nothing re-mained standing. Even the scattering cattle were gunned down – an important tactical point. Starving people might be easier to subdue; with the livestock destroyed, the rebels would be forced to come down from their remote mountain strong-holds and forage in the lowlands, clear of fog and perilous winds. There, the helicopter gunships could hunt for them at leisure.

After the raid, Radio Kabul proudly announced:

'Early this morning our brave troops destroyed an important rebel stronghold near Banu.'

The 'brave troops' consisted of two Afghan Army officers of Babrak Karmal's puppet army, riding in the Soviet heli-copters to direct the invaders against their own people. The 'important rebel stronghold' comprised three dozen primitive dwellings, 'held' by 122 elderly men, women and children, of whom only eighteen survived the sudden rain of explosives.

When the gunships departed, two Russian tanks and five Afghan Army troop carriers – which had been waiting for the signal that the road to the village was clear – moved in to finish the job, to gun down the wounded and the handful of fugitives who fled over the bare, rugged slopes. The survivors were decimated by machine gun and mortar fire.

The road to the hamlet had been open ever since Ali Ghazi Khan and his *mojahedins* left twelve days ago, to attack a supply dump on the Kabul-Doshi road. There were no guerrillas or weapons in the village which the 'friends' totally destroyed. It was a wanton act of brutality, probably done to intimidate the local population living close to the important main highway to the USSR and the vital Salang tunnel.

This and similar raids formed the cornerstone of Soviet strategy. Since the invaders could not force the Afghans to lay down their weapons and resign themselves to Communist rule, they tried to demoralise them so deeply that in the end they would prefer to give up the struggle and accept Communism as an alternative to total destruction.

When Reza and Muharrem returned and found the bodies of their parents, and their little brothers and sisters, they could only stand and stare, petrified. The boys had already witnessed similar disasters during the past eight months – they had become part of the daily routine of rural life ever since the invaders came. The Russians and Karmal's traitors held the cities and sections of the main roads with a few villages around them; the rest of the country still belonged to the free Afghans and the *mojahedins*.

But where the Russians had established themselves, their well-greased propaganda machine went to work without delay. The Kremlin dispatched a few dozen tractors and other agricultural machines bedecked with red banners, the sides lettered in Pushto: 'Gift of the Soviet Union'. Amidst great publicity, they were magnanimously handed over to local collaborators. And in the countryside the MiGs and helicopter gunships bombed and destroyed without mercy.

Reza and Muharrem drove the flock into a broken enclosure, made what repairs they could to the fence, and

16

then began the sad duty of washing and burying their dead, as the Koran commanded, before the noon prayer.

It was not a pleasant task to undress and wash the bodies of their male elders, disfigured by splinters of steel and stone and caked with blood. Their mothers and sisters they could not touch and there were no women left in the hamlet to perform the ritual, so the boys cleaned only their faces and hands. Little Aysha, Muharrem's seven-year-old sister, had her abdomen ripped open and the wound buzzed with flies. She must have suffered terribly: she had dirtied herself in her agony and the marks of her clawing fingers were visible in the dust. Muharrem could not leave her like that. He hauled fresh water from the nearby well, washed her and wrapped a strip of linen around her abdomen. Collecting all the white linen they could find, the boys wrapped the bodies, bound the bundles with string and wire, then took the *abdes* – washed themselves thoroughly and sat over their family chanting the *duva*, the prayer for the dead.

Digging graves would have been beyond them, but there was no need to dig: the 'friends of the Afghan people' had provided the hamlet with enough craters. But the boys had to hurry – the sun was already high.

Zahor Reza hated the Karmalist collaborators even more than he loathed the Russians. Everyone knew the Russians were the enemy, doubly infidel because they did not even believe in God; but that Afghan soldiers should help the invaders in their butchery was beyond his comprehension. Ali Ghazi Khan was right, he thought, when he said: 'Communists have no flag except Russia's with the hammer and sickle. They will serve that even if it means besmirching their own national flag, or the destruction of their own homeland.'

The boys spent the rest of the day picking up bodies and severed limbs: some of the victims had been horribly mangled by the tracked vehicles which had driven over them. Numbly, Reza and Muharrem laid the sad remains of neighbours, relatives and friends in common graves facing Mecca. The Koran forbade covering them before next sunrise.

They searched the ruins for food and found some flour,

sugar and rice and a hunk of roast lamb – enough for a day or two. Reza went to look for his father's old shotgun and a bazooka which he had taken from a dead Russian near Banu with the conical projectile still fitted. He wanted to give it to the *mojahedins* of the Khawak Pass.

With Muharrem's help he pulled out the weapons from the debris and cleaned and wiped them with a greasy cloth. There were sixteen cartridges for the shotgun, made in Peshawar. 'Sixteen Russians, with Allah's help,' Reza said grimly. 'Enough to begin with.'

Muharrem nodded.

'Insallah,' he said, 'if Allah wills it. I want to spend the rest of my life killing Russians. A hundred Russians for each person in the village.'

'Perhaps they will stay long enough to satisfy you,' said Reza. 'Now, we'd better eat something. I'm so tired I can't even lift the bag.'

They boiled rice and ate a hunk of roast lamb with onions.

'Where do you want to go tomorrow?' Muharrem asked.

Reza gestured towards the distant hills. 'Up to the Khawak – to join Ali Ghazi Khan.'

'What about the sheep?'

'We'll take them along with us. The *mojahedins* always need food.'

'When we've finished this let's have another look round,' Muharrem suggested. 'We might find something useful.'

Reza agreed.

He spotted a plastic water-can and went to fetch it. He tasted from it, drank, then filled his leather carrier.

'We can get fresh water from the well,' Muharrem said, puzzled, but Reza shook his head.

'The infidels might have poisoned it . . . Sometimes they do. It's safer to drink from the can, even if the water's stale and warm.'

'You think of everything,' Muharrem said appreciatively.

Reza gave him a faint smile. 'You have to think, if you want to survive nowadays.'

After the meal the boys returned to the heaps of debris to wander around, poking here and there, lifting timbers and broken doors, shifting stones. Muharrem found a bag of tea and a kettle. Reza came across a long knife. He tucked it into his belt.

When they reached the road, Muharrem saw that it was churned up with tank tracks. Squatting on his heels, he studied a deep furrow.

'The tank went towards the Pass,' he said knowledgeably. 'It should be still somewhere uphill.'

Reza dropped on one knee and traced the marks with his finger.

'You're right,' he said. 'It didn't come back – but it could never have crossed the Pass. The *mojahedins* of Ghazi Khan would destroy it . . .If they haven't done so already, then the tank will have to come back this way.'

'We should try to hit it with your bazooka.'

'Yes – this is a good place to chance it,' said Reza. 'The Russians think there isn't a soul alive here . . . '

'Do you know how to handle that thing?'

Reza bit his lip, and shrugged. 'I saw it in the cinema when my father took me to Haibak . . . You hold it on your shoulder, aim and pull the trigger – that's all there is to it.'

'If you miss, we won't have a second round.'

'And if I don't miss we won't need a second round,' Reza retorted. 'You look scared.'

'I am – a bit,' Muharrem admitted. 'I wouldn't be if we had another round, or some petrol.'

'The Russians won't know how many rounds we have, nor how many we are,' Reza pointed out, trying to cheer him up. 'Even if I miss, the infidels won't be coming out to look for us. There might be fifty *mojahedins* among the ruins.'

'They could also kill us with their machine guns.'

'The *mojahedins* say that machine guns cannot fire at targets too close, or sideways. We shall have to stay on the flank and close.'

'If the tank stopped for a moment, you'd definitely be able to hit it,' said Muharrem.

'Yes that's true.' Thoughtfully, Reza surveyed the devastated area. He spotted something round under the rubble and went to fetch it. It was a frying pan with a crookedly twisted handle. Reza waggled it back and forth, the handle snapped. Flushed with a sudden idea he turned and put his hand on Muharrem's shoulder.

'I think I know a way to stop the tank.' He waved the pan.

'How?' Muharrem demanded, and Reza winked. 'With some mines on the road.'

The younger boy stared at him. 'We haven't got any mines.'

Reza chuckled. 'The Russians won't know that, either.' He gestured with the pan. 'Here's our mine . . . Come on! We've got to look for pots and pans, all about the same size.'

Still startled, Muharrem followed.

'We're going to bury the pans in the road, poking out a bit,' Reza explained. 'The Russians will probably take them for mines and stop.'

Muharrem grinned happily. 'Great! They'll be afraid of blowing up. The infidels are scared in our country.'

'The more scared they are, the better,' said Reza.

They searched through the rubble once more and soon collected a heap of pots and pans which Reza arranged in a zig-zag pattern over about ten yards, partly covered with earth. He backed away and surveyed his 'minefield'. It looked convincing enough. No, the enemy would never drive across that lot without investigating.

He selected a good position fifteen yards from the road, behind a pile of fallen timbers and stones, and positioned the bazooka between some broken rafters, pointing to the spot where he thought the tank would stop.

'Remember not to stand behind me when I fire,' he cautioned Muharrem. 'This weapon has a vicious backfire.'

By dusk there was still no sign of the tank and Zahor Reza decided that they might as well turn in for the night. No Russian would ever move in the country during the hours of darkness. The night belonged to the *mojahedins*. Not even Karmal's arse-lickers went abroad after dusk.

'Perhaps the tank *was* destroyed in the Pass,' Muharrem ventured as they settled down in a derelict hut near the road.

'I don't think the Russians would be stupid enough to roll into the Khawak alone. They've probably driven into the middle of an open field with a good view in every direction, to wait for dawn. When they return, with Allah's help, we'll knock out the tank, find Ghazi Khan and kill more infidels.'

'Insallah,' Muharrem agreed, 'but there are so many of them.'

'We have enough land to bury them all.'

There was ample bedding in the ruined houses for the boys to rest in comfort. They slept in turns, keeping watch over the road – just in case the tank's crew were newcomers, still unaware of the rule: never challenge the Afghan hills after dark.

But except for some stray hyenas nothing stirred in the neighbourhood at night.

The tank came shortly before sunrise, lumbering towards the ruined village, churning up earth and stones: a beast of the atomic age cast aboard in the medieval – Gulliver in Lilliput, but iron-shod and far from benevolent. It seemed to be growing all the time, becoming larger and larger, taking up the entire width of the road. All of a sudden it appeared impossible that the tiny shell of the bazooka could stop it.

Reza stole a glance at Muharrem who was squatting on a pile of rubble behind a twisted stove, barely breathing, but clutching the shotgun. 'Why did they ever come to our country?' Muharrem muttered, wiping his face on his sleeve.

'To liberate us from the imperialists – that's what the radio says.'

'Who are they?' Muharrem asked. 'The imperialists?'

'The Americans and the Pakistanis – and the Chinese,' Reza retorted. 'According to Babrak Karmal, there are imperialists everywhere in the hills, disguised as Afghans and speaking Pushto. As far as he's concerned, everyone who is not a Russian, or one of his arse-lickers, is an imperialist enemy . . . Karmal ought to know . . . He's a Russian himself, sent here by Moscow to fool the people and spit on the Koran.'

'Where is Moscow?'

'On the other side of the world – may Allah raze it to the

21

ground . . . That's where Karmal lived before coming to Kabul. He is no Afghan, he's a traitor. Whoever lives with the Russian infidels is no longer what he used to be. They say the Russians can twist your mind in any way they want.'

'You know an awful lot more than I do,' said Muharrem.

Reza chuckled. 'You know I went to school in Doshi before the infidels came . . . Sssh! . . . It's getting close.'

Huge and powerful, the tank rolled over a broken cart, squashed a dead mule and came to a grinding halt twenty yards from Reza's 'mines', almost in line with the bazooka. 'It works!' Muharrem exulted, but Reza no longer paid any attention to him; his right eye was glued to the target, a section of armour just above the tracked wheels. The turret with the long gun slowly turned towards the hecatomb of ruins, searching for a victim like some prehistoric beast; moments later its heavy frontal machine guns opened up, spraying the road with systematic precision, tossing earth and stone, dislodging some of the buried pans and pots.

Reza wet his lips and pulled the trigger.

Nothing.

'The safety lock!'

It came to him in a flash and he flipped it over with trembling fingers. The driver must have realised that the 'mines' were harmless: the gears grumbled, the engine changed pitch and the tank advanced, with one machine gun still rattling, knocking the 'mines' off the road.

Reza fired again.

He felt the recoil, saw a thin, grey trail going to the tank, heard a dull thud followed by a muffled explosion. An instant later, flames burst from the stricken monster.

Muharrem leapt to his feet. 'You killed it! You killed it!' he yelled excitedly. 'Allah akhbar, Allah is great . . . '

Grabbing him by an arm, Reza pulled him down.

'Keep low, you crazy goat!'

'You hit it right in the belly!' Muharrem cried, and rose again, shaking the old shotgun above his head.

'Watch out!' Reza yelled, and yanked him down as the turret-hatch was flung open and a dark, helmeted shape, with his uniform burning, emerged half-way, shrieking unintelligibly. 'Shoot!' Reza yelled. Muharrem took a hasty aim and fired. With a wild animal cry, the Russian rolled on to the frontal armour with part of his face torn away. The flames leapt, and dark, oily smoke belched from the tank. 'His pistol,' Muharrem croaked, scrambling down. 'We must get his pistol.'

Reza grabbed him again. 'Stay where you are. There must be four or five infidels in a big tank like this.'

'The others must be dead,' Muharrem argued. 'It must be like hell inside.'

'Wait!'

Muharrem obeyed, but still arguing. 'If the others aren't dead yet, they'll have to come out, or fry.'

Trrrrr ... trrrrr ... The savage stutter of a machine pistol raked the debris around the boys, tearing splinters of wood and masonry. 'Someone else has come out,' Muharrem whispered. 'How?'

'There must be a second hatch! Perhaps on the far side, or underneath.'

Muharrem peered through a gap in the pile of rubble. 'He's underneath, near the back,' he said, and sprang down as the Russian fired again.

'He cannot hit us here,' Reza spoke reassuringly.

Muharrem crawled back to the hole.

'Can you see him?' Reza asked, scanning the road.

'Now – yes ... He's trying to crawl forward.'

'It must be getting hot under there,' Reza said gleefully. 'Give me the gun.'

Rising a little he took aim and fired. The shower of birdshot sent the Russian scurrying back behind the rear wheels.

'Stay put,' Reza told Muharrem. 'I'll try and cross the road.'

'Suppose that Russian comes here?'

'He won't. He knows there's a gun here ... Throw some stones to distract him.'

He crawled away, swiftly as a lizard, and Muharrem began to throw stones at the tank, drawing a few more salvoes; then

23

he spotted a length of broken pipe and pushed it through the opening. The Russian saw it and, thinking it was a weapon, fired again. 'Keep shooting,' Muharrem mumbled to himself. Perhaps by the time Reza had got to the other side of the road, the enemy would have run out of bullets. Then the thought came to him: 'What if he has a grenade?' and a sudden wave of heat flooded his chest and face. Bending low, he scurried behind a partly crumbled wall at a healthier distance, but kept throwing stones.

Inside the burning tank the machine gun ammunition began to explode, singly, then in series. The Russian started to crawl in the other direction. Reza got there just in time to catch him partly exposed. He fired and the man cried out as he was hit in the legs. In the tank the cartridges exploded like firecrackers, blowing more fire and smoke through the hatch. Reza suspected that the heavy shells would soon follow. The Russian must have thought the same. There was no way out of his predicament, with a gun in front of him, another one somewhere in the ruins, and sixty tons of steel threatening to blow up overhead.

'Nie strilay! – 'don't shoot!' he yelled. He tossed his machine pistol into the open and rose.

'Hore ruki!' Reza commanded and his enemy raised his hands.

'Stoy!'

The Russian froze. Covering him with the shotgun, Reza snatched up the machine pistol. 'Idi – davai, davai,' he urged his prisoner, motioning towards the ruins. 'Forward! Move!'

Muharrem rushed to the tank and wrenched the automatic from the fingers of the dead man.

'Get away from there!' Reza shouted as more vicious flames burst from the turret. 'It'll blow up any minute.'

Tucking the pistol into his belt, Muharrem joined Reza. Dragging and pushing the terrified Russian they retreated into the ruins.

'Take his pistol, too, you goat,' Reza scowled at his friend; he'd just noticed the prisoner was still carrying his belt and holster. Muharrem took it and belted it on. The prisoner sank on to a boulder and struggled to tie a length of cord round his bleeding left leg. Neither of the boys felt like helping him.

'*Vratch, vratch,*' he groaned and Reza said to Muharrem, 'He's asking for a doctor.' Turning to the Russian he said fiercely: 'We have no doctors here . . . *Niema vratch* – and the more you bleed the better.'

'You know his language?' the younger boy asked.

'Enough to tell him where to go,' Reza replied with contempt. 'My father used to know some Russian smugglers who sometimes slept in our house. But they were cheerful sort of chaps, who liked to have a drink, and a good time . . . Not like the marauders who come here with guns . . . Wounded Russians are always crying for *vratch* – the healthy ones ask for *chasi*, a watch. It's the first thing the thieves demand when they take someone prisoner. They all have watches, but they prefer our Japanese ones – they even know the name. "Seiko, Seiko," they go.'

He turned to the prisoner. '*Davai chasi.*' The Russian took off his wristwatch and handed it over.

The boy examined it. 'Russian-made,' he said, and pursed his lip. 'He must be a newcomer . . . Had no chance to steal yet, only to kill people.'

He poked the prisoner in the ribs. '*Idi!* – Move!' and the man limped as he was pushed across a heap of rubble, into the ruins of a yard, blotched with dry blood, and pitifully littered with the bodies of dogs, hens and donkeys. Reza pushed the Russian to the edge of the mass grave, with its rows of white bundles. 'One hundred and fifteen people,' he snarled in his broken Russian. 'No hospital, no doctor. Only death.'

Pale and shaking the prisoner stared at Reza, and wiped the sweat, mingled with dust and blood, from his face, '*Voina nie haraso,*' he muttered. '*Mir haraso.*'

Reza agreed with him. 'War is no good, peace is good. We didn't ask you to make war on us.' He pointed into the tragic pit. 'My mother, my father, my little sister . . . All dead. And now *you* shall die.'

The Russian understood him and became even paler as he suddenly realised that he had come a long way to die in this

25

remote, godforsaken village, which – according to his political officer – 'crawled with armed rebels, led by the CIA agents and Pakistani Army officers'.

'Our Koran decrees an eye for an eye, a tooth for a tooth,' Reza said grimly. 'Invaders who come to Afghanistan *die*. They all die. Today, tomorrow, next year . . . Few of you infidels will ever return home.'

The barrel of his gun came up. The Russian recoiled, and flung up his arms. '*Nie strilay!*' he screamed and Reza shot him in the neck; he fell to the ground and lay, twitching spasmodically, blood spurting from the severed arteries. Lifting a foot, Reza rolled his dying enemy from the make-shift grave. 'His blood should not mingle with that of our loved ones,' he said grimly. Muharrem drew his newly acquired automatic, as thought wanting to deliver the *coup de grace*, but Reza laid a restraining hand on his arm. 'No, Muharrem . . . We need every bullet for the living enemy. This one here is already dead, or will be, after a few more kicks.'

Muharrem nodded, holstered the pistol and reached for the snub-nosed machine pistol. He peered at the lettering. 'What does it say here?'

'P . . . M . . . sixty-three . . . Poland,' Reza spelled out what he understood.

'Where is Poland?' Muharrem asked.

Reza shrugged. 'Allah knows . . . Somewhere in Russia, like Uzbekistan.'

'Allah is good,' Muharrem said. 'He gave us good weapons and plenty of cartridges. When we find Ghazi Khan, we'll be welcome.'

Reza squatted down and frisked the corpse's pockets. He found a pen, money, cigarettes, a lighter and five photos.

'His wife and children.' He showed the pictures to Muharrem. 'His wife is now a widow and his children are orphans – like us . . . He has a family, yet he comes here to murder our families.'

'A soldier must go where he is sent,' Muharrem said quietly.

Reza spat. 'How many of the Karmalists have come over to our side, instead of shooting us?'

'But this one was a Russian – not even a Moslem . . . '

'Still, he could have aimed badly when he fired against our people,' said Reza. 'It's easy for a gunner to miss when he wants to.'

'That's true,' Muharrem conceded.

'The Russians don't want to miss,' Reza continued. 'They enjoy killing . . . Come, let us bury the dead.'

Three hours later the boys left the ruined village. Herding the flock of sheep, hauling their booty, they set out for the Khawak Pass, where Reza hoped to find Ali Ghazi Khan and his famous *mojahedins*. He had no doubt about being accepted. One Russian tank, a pair of pistols, one sub-machine gun and a couple of dead infidel invaders were good enough reference, not to mention the sheep.

Zahor Reza and Muharrem Zarag were far from being the only youngsters in the camp of Ali Ghazi Khan. It had become the local refuge for some sixty orphans of the air raids and bombardments. The youngest were still babies, but most were between six and twelve, boys and girls whom fear and tragedy had turned into little adults: never playing, rarely laughing, nourished by one ambition – revenge. The teenagers learned to assemble and handle bombs and mines and a great variety of weapons, ranging from early nine-teenth-century French Lebel rifles to First World War vintage British Enfields. Young girls helped to make bandages from strips of linen and the silk of captured para-chutes, and tended to their smaller companions and the wounded guerrillas.

Every now and then, when there was a lull and the trails were safe, mule trains of twenty to fifty children would be escorted to the Mommand Mountains, to Haydar Chari, whose *mojahedins* would take them across the frontier into a safe refugee camp in Pakistan. But the number of youngsters in the Khawak seldom dropped below forty, as more and more little orphans were rescued by the guerrillas from the devastated hamlets.

When Reza and Muharrem arrived, Ali Ghazi Khan and his men had already been informed of the latest Russian outrage. The look-outs had also spotted the solitary tank which dared the precipitous road to the Khawak Pass. Ghazi and a dozen *mojahedins* at once set off down a dangerous slope to get it from the flank, planning to attack when the tank stopped at the old stone bridge it couldn't possibly cross. But the enemy commander must have been well informed, because he stopped two miles short of the bridge. Under cover of darkness, he manoeuvred the tank into a derelict stone quarry and spent the night there camouflaged with shrubs. The guerrilla search party missed it completely: there were scores of smaller and larger caves along the road, and by the time Ghazi found the right one in the first light of dawn, the tank was gone.

When the *mojahedins* of the Khawak learned that the tank had been stopped and destroyed at the 'minefield' laid by Reza and Muharrem, the boys were given a tumultuous reception. Ghazi Khan sent a salvage party to recover the heavy turret machine gun and whatever else the flames might have spared. To his delight, the men returned with the gun, some cartridges, another pistol and a box of twelve fragmentation shells. Fitted with fins, the artillery shells could be hurled by hand from high overhangs on to enemy troops and vehicles advancing below, and would work like bombs.

Lacking the proper weapons, the *mojahedins* had of necessity grown inventive. In their long war of attrition against the superbly equipped invader, they used bows, dynamite and home-made 'grenades' – ordinary clay pots filled with gunpowder and rusty nails – as well as vintage weapons.

Daring individuals and small groups of desperate men began to raid Karmalist police stations. They held up Afghan Army patrols and snatched modern weapons; with their help, they were able to seize more. Automatic weapons came through secret channels: from the warlike Pathans and

Marris of Baluchistan, from friendly sources in Iran and from Red China. But except for the 'moral support' of a few carefully worded and feebly delivered 'protests', the great pillars of the free democracies offered no practical assistance to the embittered Afghans, who rightly complained that whenever, somewhere in the world, twenty Marxists gathered to fight the United States, Britain, or France, the Kremlin would promptly support them with sophisticated weapons and money, but when an oppressed people rose against Soviet oppression, no one would lift a finger to help them for fear that the Russian bear might start to growl, even to bite.

THE HELICOPTER GUNSHIP

'HOW CAN we lose the war when we have youngsters like Reza and Muharrem?' Ali Ghazi Khan asked the lanky Englishman. 'And we have thousands like them.'

Jim nodded. 'I believe you,' he said. 'I've spent some time in Pakistan, near Quetta. The Pathans of the Lorelai range there have boys of ten equipped with rifles and bandoliers . . . '

Reza and Muharrem were smiling modestly, obviously pleased with their new status as *mojahedins*, with a Russian tank to their credit.

'The Pathans of Pakistan and many of the Afghans are blood-brothers,' said Ali Ghazi Khan. 'The invaders are going to have a hard time here.'

They were sitting beneath a rocky overhang, smoking and drinking tea after a long trek. At thirty-seven, Ali Ghazi Khan was the inspiring leader of some three hundred guerrillas operating in Nuristan and Kohistan. He was a small, stocky man with a closely-trimmed beard, whose round face and high forehead, and dark, dancing eyes were all dominated by a prominent, hawkish nose which suggested a strong, commanding personality and unbending will. He had been a teacher in Jalalabad until the Russians occupied the town and Babrak Karmal, the Soviet puppet, was made President. He ordered schools to teach less about Islam, and Afghanistan's royalist and bourgeois-democratic past, and more about her Marxist-Leninist future, under the brotherly leadership of the USSR. Ali Ghazi opted for discussing the future with a gun in his hand against the godless invaders and their collaborators, and he was not alone. Thousands of able men, many of them past middle age, chose to resist the new, alien regime. Some three hundred of them formed a group and elected Ali Ghazi as leader. With all the arms and ammunition they could find, the men moved into the remote, hostile mountains of the Panjshir valley which some of them had known well since early childhood.

Zafar Ghazi, thirty-two, was Ali's impetuous younger brother. He was a deserter from the ever-diminishing Afghan Army, leaving three days after the Soviet 'advisers' took command. Ghazi's right hand was Ahmad Mazar. In his early fifties, he was a giant of a man, but although he carried great authority, his manner was gentle and mild. Mazar was good-humoured and sharp-witted, and his deep, booming voice could be heard above the noisiest crowd. A former blacksmith in Haibak, near the Soviet border, Mazar had lost his wife and baby during a MiG attack, but had managed to get his mother and four children across the border to Pakistan. On his return, he joined the *mojahedins* of the Khawak.

The lanky pipe-smoking Englishman with the short red beard had come over from Peshawar 'to lend a hand' to the guerrillas. 'Just call me Jim,' he'd told them. 'The rest is in my passport but I left it on the other side of the border – I don't suppose Karmal will be handing out many visas these days.'

'What were you doing in Pakistan?' asked Ali Ghazi.

'Oh, nothing dramatic . . . My wife and I have a little shop in London selling Oriental stuff – every now and then I go on a buying trip.'

'To Pakistan?'

'Pakistan, India, Nepal, Thailand . . . I've been to Afghanistan before. They're very fond of Oriental stuff at home – old prayer rugs, saddlebags, vases, religious masks, copper and bronze cooking things, old weapons . . . They all go down well.'

'Then you've come to the right place, Jim,' boomed Ahmad Mazar.

'And no Customs,' Ali Ghazi chuckled, 'at least not for the time being.'

'That's important,' Jim said with a grin.

'We'll get you some old guns – all hand-made – '

'Silver-worked and inlaid with camel-bone,' the Englishman cut in. 'I have a few guns at home. They are very popular among collectors. Got them in India.'

'And the Indians told you they were pure ivory?' asked Mazar.

Jim grinned again. 'Well, they tried . . . '

'You see, we're honest . . . Are you interested?'

'I'm always interested in genuine antiques.'

The talk turned to the invasion.

Ali Ghazi Khan had been in Kabul on the gloomy late December day in 1979 when the snow-bound city woke to the roar of heavy engines. The airport resounded with incoming Soviet aircraft: helicopters and huge Antonov transports crowded the airspace and landed one after another, discharging troops and troop-carriers, artillery and light tanks. Before the people realised what was happening, the Russians had moved in to seize every important installation in and around the capital. The radio, the telecommunications centre, the police headquarters and sections of the main road were all taken over, and the Afghan Army barracks were surrounded by Soviet tanks. The three-month government of Hafizullah Amin was abruptly terminated. Amin, though a Communist backed by Moscow, had perhaps too many nationalistic tendencies for Soviet liking: he disappeared in the dustbin of Communist history. A few days later the Afghans learned that they had elected a new President in the obscure person of Babrak Karmal – an expatriate handed back by the Russians after a long sojourn in Moscow.

Babrak's first act was to root out all those who had been known for their patriotism, religious fervour and anti-Communist attitude. Thousands of people were taken into custody; thousands went underground, or fled into the hills.

'I'd been suspicious ever since the Russians began building the main highway to the USSR and "helping" us to develop our natural gas resources,' Ali Ghazi said grimly. 'They never do anything without long-term plans, and they'd never help anyone unless they could help themselves in the process. Twelve years later, the truth came out. They had built the road to make the invasion easier, and all the gas from our fields goes straight to the USSR without them paying a penny. It's set against the Red Army's bills for their stay in Afghanistan. Needless to say, we'll always be in the red. The Russians are Communists only at home. When it comes to ripping off other countries, they're bigger capitalists than Rockefeller.

'Karmal's troops don't give us any sleepless nights, though,' Ali Ghazi Khan went on with satisfaction. 'The real soldiers of the Afghan Army have long since deserted, or fled to Pakistan, or joined the *mojahedins*. All that's left is a scared, confused lot of opportunists and raw recruits, who were pretty well forced to join up at gun-point . . . And we're not scared of the Russians, either. Brezhnev doesn't feel like having the cream of his troops decimated, and most of this lot are Siberian rubbish, the dregs of Soviet society – they haven't got a clue what war is about. They can't think for themselves, they just follow orders. When we knock off their sergeants or corporals they're like a flock of lost sheep in the hills, surrounded by wolves. Of course, they have good training, but shooting at a scoreboard, and shooting at targets which shoot back, are two different things. And much of what they learned at home, in the training camps, doesn't apply at all in a country like Afghanistan.'

Ali Ghazi Khan paused to fill his pipe. He offered the Englishman some tobacco, then went on quietly, drinking his tea: 'The officers aren't much better, either. Their only battle experience comes from heroic armoured drives against East European stone-throwing students in the satellite countries. Oh, yes – the Russians are great heroes in Eastern Europe, where everyone is scared of them. Here in Afghanistan they're the ones who are scared. They daren't go out after dark, even in Kabul. They suspect every smiling face, see a trap in every dark corner. They know they are not only alien invaders, but infidels – enemies not only of the Afghans, but of Allah. They've already killed too many people, and they know full well that every doorway, every window, every little alley can hide a man desperate for revenge . . . If you hurt an Afghan he will not die until he has had his revenge, even if he has to die himself in the process. An eye for an eye is an age-old law here. When the Russians are forced to spend a night in an occupied village they stay inside their tanks and armoured cars and keep the hatches locked. They don't dare to come out even for a piss – though we rather like killing them when they go to relieve themselves and let them lie in their own filth . . . – The heroes of Communism! They're all very brave when a thousand of them roar through a village with machine guns and grenades, cheering and shooting down women and children and old people. But in the dead of night they're scared stiff.'

'We're not afraid of the tanks, either,' Ahmad Mazar cut in, rubbing his heard. 'We lure them to places where they cannot even turn round, and when we have nothing better, we bury them under tons of earth and stones . . . ' He turned to Jim. 'You wouldn't believe how the Russians fall into the simplest traps – very few of their tanks ever return from the hills.'

It's only the helicopters which give us real trouble,' Ali Ghazi Khan added grimly. 'Copters are fast and can go almost everywhere in the mountains . . . The only thing in our favour is the morning fog . . . We have nothing to fight the copters with. *Nothing*.'

'Ever tried a bazooka?' Jim asked casually. The men looked at him blankly. Then a few burst out laughing.

'You chaps think I'm a nitwit, don't you?'

'What's a nitwit?' asked Ali.

'An idiot.'

Ahmad Mazar rocked with laughter. 'No, you're not an idiot, my infidel friend.' He slapped the Englishman on the back. 'I expect you first got a touch of sunstroke when you climbed up here.'

Jim looked at him. 'Have you ever been attacked by a helicopter gunship, Ahmad?'

Mazar grinned. 'Twice! And it was hot, too.'

'And what did you do?'

'Hide!'

The men roared, but Jim said calmly: 'I know of a Cornish bloke who downed a copter in Korea with a hand-grenade.'

'While it was on the ground with the crew asleep,' said Mazar, raising more laughter.

34

'While it was flying happily,' said Jim.

'Are you joking?' Zafar Ghazi asked.

'Why should I be?'

The laughter died down. 'Tell us about it, Jim,' Ali Ghazi prompted.

Jim shrugged. 'There really isn't much to it, Ali. It happened over very similar terrain – near a ravine.' He picked up a twig, and drawing in the dust, illustrated the story of five British soldiers and two Americans holed up in a rock-face, covering a stone bridge which the North Koreans wanted to cross. 'The reds had already lost a tank and a few lorries, so they called for copters,' he told them. 'The one which came was flown by a Russian volunteer who made a few low passes, trying to fire into the cave – very tricky, having to manoeuvre between the rocks. The pilot was quite skilled but in his enthusiasm he went too close to the cave. And this Cornish chap, suddenly inspired, hurled a grenade which exploded in front of the cockpit. The copter crashed.'

The men were silent. Then Zafar Ghazi said: 'I think if the circumstances were right, it could be done. Why not?'

Jim nodded. 'You're damned right . . . And a bazooka shell can go a hell of a lot further than a grenade.'

Ali Ghazi Khan slapped him on the knee.

'I think we should try it.'

'Why shouldn't you? You've got the ravine – wide enough for a copter to negotiate. There's the cliff, with a good cave to guard the road . . . In fact you've got *two* caves, haven't you? One almost level with the road, the other one higher up. That should make it all much easier.'

'Why?' asked Mazar.

'Well, didn't you say that the Russians would be coming up here soon, and that you would try and stop them in the valley? I think if you use the lower cave as a decoy, the Russians will open fire on it . . . Come on, let's go and have a look.' Beckoning Ali Ghazi and his companions to the slope down to the narrow road, he tried to show what he meant. The *mojahedins* followed, no longer treating the whole thing as a joke, but intrigued: the prospect of downing an enemy copter filled them with excitement. The helicopter gunships were the arch enemy: safe from the primitive local weapons, they flew in deadly freedom over the countryside.

'Right. Now imagine a column of tanks, lorries and infantry moving along the road,' said Jim. 'You have two men in the upper cave with the bazooka, but they don't show themselves. You open fire from the lower cave, letting the enemy spot you and think you have a stronghold there, capable of blocking their advance . . . Have a look down below. The tanks will never be able to hit the cave from there.'

'True.' Ali Ghazi surveyed the site. 'If we manage to convince them that we have anti-tank weapons in the cave, they'll be bound to halt on the slope.'

Mazar cut in. 'And perhaps call for MiGs to bomb the road.'

'MiGs my foot,' said Jim. 'The Russians won't bomb the only road they can advance on.'

'This place is strong enough to stop a whole division,' Zafar Ghazi said thoughtfully.

Jim grinned. 'You're not kidding. This is *the* place to stop the enemy. And when the convoy can't advance any further, the commander will call for copters . . . But the ravine is too narrow – only one copter can operate in it at once. If the pilot wants to attack the decoy cave, he'll have to pass pretty close to the upper one . . . At a distance of fifteen yards, I should say. That's nothing for a good fellow with a bazooka – be like hitting a slow-moving tank from a ditch.'

Ali Ghazi's face broke into a happy grin of anticipation and the *mojahedins* began to cheer wildly. Ahmad Mazar slapped the Englishman on the back. 'Masallah, you haven't got sunstroke, Jim,' he roared. It's a pity you're an infidel dog – but you're a good one . . . ' He caught him in his powerful bearhug. 'Masallah.'

'We have only one bazooka and five rounds to go with it,' Ghazi reminded his men.

'The Russians won't know that,' Jim pointed out. 'Keep your aim true. Fire two rounds from the decoy cave to stop the enemy . . . If you're lucky you might even hit something.

36

Then hurry into the upper cave and wait for the copters, but keep firing from the decoy. Let them see where the trouble is coming from.'

Ali Ghazi Khan thought it over, scratched his bearded chin, then looked at him levelly.

'Jim, did you say you were in the British Army?'

'That's right – for two bloody years.'

'Hmmm,' Ali grunted. 'Why won't *you* handle our bazooka?'

'And get into trouble with my Embassy in Islamabad?' Jim chuckled. 'I'm supposed to be neutral, Ali.'

Ghazi threw up his arms. 'How can anyone remain neutral when the Russians are involved? They want to grab the whole world – even Hitler didn't go that far . . . If what's happening in Afghanistan doesn't convince you, think of the free countries they've taken over – directly or indirectly.'

'Before Karmal came,' Zafar Ghazi cut in, 'we never even heard the word Communist in Afghanistan. Ali is right – no thinking person can remain neutral in a world threatened by the Russians.'

Ali Ghazi took Jim's arm. 'When you came to us, you said you wanted to give us a hand . . . Now about handling that bazooka?'

'My dear Ali, I'm no anti-tank expert.'

'But you *have* used a bazooka before . . . '

'Well, it's part of the basic infantry training in the British Army . . . A couple of times, yes, but it didn't turn me into a Robin Hood with the bazooka.'

Ali Ghazi Khan shrugged. 'In *our* army,' he said with a smile, 'we show the recruit how to toss bottles of petrol . . . Jim, we cannot afford to waste ammunition, especially not bazooka shells . . . Be reasonable.'

'It's not much to ask,' Zafar added persuasively.

'Quite enough for the Russians I might hit . . . '

'The Russians will never know.' Zafar waved aside the hesitant objection.

'Never know, my foot,' Jim protested. 'With a hundred of your people watching the show? Some of them might be taken prisoner one day and talk.'

'None of our *mojahedins* would ever talk,' Mazar's indignation was obvious.

'You don't know the GRU, Ahmad.'

'What is the GRU?'

'The Soviet Military Intelligence – and they can make a dead canary sing.'

'We need your help.' Zafar hammered at the theme.

Jim cast a hard look at Ghazi, then grinned. 'Well, all right, blast you, if I only *aimed* and someone else pulled the trigger . . . ' He left the sentence unfinished.

'You do the aiming,' Ghazi said cheerfully. 'Mazar shall do the shooting and you will preserve your neutrality.'

'It won't make any difference to the Russian firing squad, though.'

Ahmad Mazar spat. 'Jim, my infidel friend,' he boomed, 'I have been killing Russians for six months and sent at least fifty of them to hell, but I haven't been shot yet.'

'There's always a first time, and once is enough.'

'You do the aiming?'

'I'll do it – and damned if I let the Ivans catch me.'

'I knew you wouldn't let us down,' Ali Ghazi exulted. 'We have quite a few foreigners helping us. Not fighting though; we have enough men to do the killing. Our foreigners are helping us with advice and medicine. We have a French and a German physician, two nurses, and a British couple who are trying to invent something to use against the copters . . . so they say.'

'Who says so?' asked Jim.

'The *mojahedins* of Haydar Chari – in the Mommands range, near the Pakistani border.'

Jim thought they must be a very peculiar couple.

'Why don't you bring them here?'

Ghazi shook his head. 'It would be unwise, Jim. Haydar Chari keeps them close to the border, just in case the Russians or a few Karmalists turn up unexpectedly in the Mommands. Neither the Russians, nor Karmal's traitors can hold any land in the mountains, but their commandos can always land by helicopter, slaughter a few dozen people and leave before we can hit back . . . So, we keep those two close to the border.'

'What are their names?'

'We know them as Alister and Natalie. Perhaps those are their real names, perhaps not. We're not interested in names, only in goodwill.'

'And they're working on something which will bring down a copter?'

'Yes.'

'If we had a few rapid-fire guns,' said Zafar Ghazi, 'we could cope with the copters and perhaps with the MiGs too.' He paused. 'Why won't your government supply us with weapons, Jim?'

The Englishman chuckled. 'Perhaps because you beat us in the Khyber about fifty years ago.' The men laughed.

'But the Americans are the same,' Mazar added when the guffaws had died down. 'The Russians supply weapons to every mob in the world ready to fight your allies. Why aren't you doing the same, and stirring up trouble for them in the countries they're interfering with?'

'Because the Russians are ruled by a dictatorship,' Jim said. 'In Great Britain it's the people who decide what the government should do – but it's hard to get them moving.'

'Are they blind?'

'They're not blind, Ali . . . But there are plenty of people who tuck themselves comfortably into their cosy little homes and couldn't really care less if a neighbour's house burns down. Especially not if it's a few streets away. They'd only start panicking when the flames were over the fence and threatening their own property.'

'That's very bad,' said Ahmad Mazar. 'Some fires can't be put out.'

'You're right,' Jim said. 'That's why we had to suffer so many initial set-backs in both wars and paid a much higher price for victory. To get an Englishman to respond to provocation, you have to give him a good kick up the arse.' He grinned. 'The British Empire is gone, but we still have our pride – a few good kicks would be enough to get us to kick back.'

'And how about the Americans?' asked Ali Ghazi. 'In a sense we are fighting for them too.'

Jim gave a grim smile. 'To tell you the truth, when it really comes down to it, I don't think anyone can ever count on America. To move Uncle Sam you have to bomb New York, or sink a fleet like the Japanese did at Pearl Harbor. The Americans never take any threat seriously until they've suffered a few thousand casualties. They are wary allies, and they have no foreign policy worth mentioning, but they do worry about their business interests getting hurt. What America does or doesn't do depends mostly on the possible reaction on Wall Street.

He observed his Afghan companions, then added gravely: 'You must learn to stand on your own feet – no one in the world will ever lift a finger to help you, Ali. It's the sad reality. No one likes the idea of provoking the Russian bear.'

'But the Russian bear can provoke anyone, anywhere,' grunted Mazar. 'The only way to stop Russian aggression is to pay them in kind. When the Red Army invaded Afghanistan, the Americans should have overrun Cuba. That would have made the Russians lose more over there than they could possibly gain here.'

Jim gave a hollow laugh. 'It's not as simple as that, Ahmad. The Soviet leader can pick up the phone and order the Red Army to move, or to fire a nuclear missile. The American President has to have the consent of the senate before he can fire as much as a protest note.'

'Unless the Russians drop a hydrogen bomb on New York first,' said Zafar Ghazi. 'A ten-megaton one.'

'Yes, that would probably rally the majority,' Jim said with a smile. 'But even then a few senators would insist on answering with only one megaton – to show the Kremlin American goodwill.'

The guerrillas laughed.

'We are not afraid of the future,' Ali Ghazi concluded. 'No invader can ever hold a country like Afghanistan – we'll fight the Communists to the bitter end.'

The enemy arrived a few days later: four tanks and twelve troop carriers with half a dozen lorries in tow. Only the troop carriers and one tank carried Soviet markings; the rest belonged to Karmal's reluctant 'army' no longer permitted to embark on any mission into the hills without an escort of Red Army 'comrades' – to prevent mass desertion if nothing else. Since the beginning of the Soviet Occupation, seventeen thousand Afghan soldiers, including sixteen hundred officers had reneged on Babrak Karmal, and fled to Pakistan and Iran. There they joined the *mojahedins*, or went into hiding in the towns.

The guerrillas of Ali Ghazi Khan were prepared for the advance. From their position at eight thousand feet on the plateau they had a good view of the valley and the winding, narrow road with the convoy labouring uphill. Familiar by now with Russian tactics, Ali Ghazi had his men well concealed in the tangle of boulders and underbrush. Not even a mule was left in the open to be spotted by the screaming MiGs and low-flying copters which the *mojahedins* allowed to scout the area undisturbed. Their reconnoitre over, the aircraft flew off, and Ahmad Mazar and Jim climbed into the narrow shaft which connected the upper cave with the plateau. It had now been fitted with a wooden ladder. Ali Ghazi, his brother and two more men occupied the cave on the roadside and waited for the convoy to reach the steep slope only four hundred yards before the last hairpin bend.

The vehicles moved very slowly. A platoon of Karmalists marched fifty yards ahead of the leading tank, searching for mines, surveying the rock-faces and roadside caves, looking for any sign of tampering. Clearly the Russians were unwilling to take any risks at all in the wild and hostile region. Ali Ghazi Khan regarded their cautious behaviour as a good sign: so wary an enemy would surely stop at the first sign of trouble.

Using the heavy machine gun salvaged from Reza and Muharrem's tank, Ghazi fired a few short salvoes against the lorries, not so much to cause damage, as to reveal the position of the decoy 'roadblock'. By sheer chance he set fire to a communications vehicle. At once, the convoy ground to a halt. The advance guard and the soldiers in the exposed trucks scattered. Lying on his stomach on the roadside precipice, Zafar Ghazi launched a bazooka shell towards the larger, Russian tank that was fourth in the row. He missed, but the troop carrier behind exploded in a vicious ball of fire, hurtling weapons, bodies and limbs in every direction. Zafar withdrew; then – safely out of sight – he raced up to the plateau and delivered the bazooka to Mazar through the shaft.

From down below, machine guns opened fire, but none of them could reach the cave, and the handful of Karmalists who attempted to negotiate the precipice quickly succumbed to Ghazi's well-placed snipers. The Russian tank fired three rounds which blasted chunks of rock from the cliff, realised the futility of the action and fell silent. The one at the head lurched forward and churned its way to the bend where an avalanche of large boulders and a drum of burning oil discouraged the driver from advancing any further.

Saving their ammunition, the *mojahedins* pestered the stationary trucks with chunks of rock rolled down the precipice, causing some damage and casualties. Harassed incessantly, the rear vehicles reversed gear and started to back away until a half-ton boulder rolled on to the road blocked them completely. The Russian tank managed to push the burning troop carrier and lorry into the ravine, but it could not reach the boulder at the back. The road was too narrow to get the lorries past. The convoy was virtually trapped.

Ali Ghazi, swore bitterly. 'If we had the proper weapons, they'd be wiped out in fifteen minutes.'

He was reluctant to use the band's handful of grenades and encouraged the men to continue to heave boulders on to the road below. The terrified yells and cries of anguish made it clear that some of the jagged rocks had found victims.

All this time Ahmad Mazar and Jim were hiding in the upper cave, watching. As they'd all expected, the MiGs returned to strafe the plateau, but they could use neither bombs nor rockets without endangering their own vehicles and men. Ten minutes later a pair of copters came clattering along the rugged course of the ravine, some three hundred yards apart. The leading one tried to manoeuvre into position to attack the decoy 'bunker', while the rear one rose above the apparently empty plateau and sprayed the rocky tangle with machine-gun salvoes.

Keeping to the dark side of the cave, Jim crawled on his elbows to the opening and positioned the bazooka on a slab of rock in front of Mazar. 'Get ready,' he whispered to Mazar who stretched out beside him, ready to fire. 'When I say *now* – fire.'

He concentrated on the copter.

The gunship hovered closer. Concentrating on the road-side cave, firing directly into it now, the Russians subjected the 'rebel stronghold' to a vicious stream of explosive slugs. Now almost stationary, the gunship presented a sure target: Jim was overjoyed – he did not want to disappoint the *mojahedins*. Obeying orders, the guerrillas refrained from sniping at it and allowed the pilot to proceed unhindered. Over the ravine the gunners submitted the dark hollow to a steady spray of tracers. A pair of rockets streaked towards the cliff; one went inside and blew a tongue of flame and billowing smoke through the opening. 'Now!' hissed Jim and Mazar pulled the trigger.

The projectile hit the cowling of the propeller shaft and ripped off the entire propulsion system. The triple-bladed shaft broke away from the fuselage; still spinning it careened into the precipice. And the gunship turned upside down, crashed into the ravine and exploded.

'Load!' Jim spoke tersely, suddenly overcome with excitement. 'We might get the tank on the bend as well, and bottle up the whole blasted road for good.'

Mazar fitted another projectile, and Jim took aim and fired too. He hit the engine compartment behind the turret and the tank began to burn. Three members of the crew scrambled out and fled towards the convoy, racing from boulder to boulder, dodging the slugs from Ali's snipers.

'You fired!' Ahmad Mazar exclaimed and his face broke into a broad grin. 'Why?'

'Because I'm an idiot,' Jim grunted, but grinning himself. 'The chance was too good to remain neutral.'

'Masallah!' Mazar complimented. 'We've still got one more shell, Jim. You ought to try your hand at something else.'

The Englishman muttered an unintelligible reply and got up.

'Let's get out of here before the Russkis fry us,' he said to Mazar, and heaved up the bazooka. The two men climbed down the shaft to the plateau. Moments later the three tanks began to shell the cave.

Zafar Ghazi helped them into the open. The second copter was nowhere in sight. 'It fled,' he said happily. 'The enemy thinks we have an anti-aircraft weapon – thanks to you.'

Jim and Mazar joined a group of *mojahedins* on a rocky ledge which gave a good view of the blocked convoy.

Puffing away at his pipe, Jim said matter-of-factly; 'Well, chaps, it hasn't been a bad day – so far. One tank, one troop carrier, three lorries and a copter . . . And some enemy casualties into the bargain . . . ' He looked at Ali Ghazi. 'What do you intend to do now?'

'What *can* we do?' asked Ghazi.

'You've got a couple of shells left for the bazooka. Use them against the large tank.'

'You can use them much better yourself,' Ahmad Mazar suggested with a wink. 'You hit the first tank right where it hurts.'

'You'd better stop your recruiting campaign, Ahmad,' Jim told him. 'I've already done my fair share for your damn cause.' He turned to Ali Ghazi. 'How many grenades have you got?'

'Twelve,' came the glum answer.

'Not many . . . Any petrol?'

'Only one can – perhaps half a gallon.'

The Briton made a vague gesture towards the ruins of a village half a mile away. 'Is there anything in the village that would burn well?'

Ghazi thought for a moment. 'A few bales of hay.'

'And charcoal,' added Mazar.

'All right. Send some men to bring it all here.'

Zafar Ghazi set off with thirty guerrillas. Jim, Ali, and Mazar kept watch on the convoy, harassed incessantly with sniper-shots whenever a trooper showed himself in the open.

The Russians were still sitting in their troop carriers with the hatches battened down.

'We don't have anything that'll get through that armour,' Ali Ghazi said in frustration.

Jim gave him an encouraging pat on the back. 'Cheer up, Ali, we'll get them out of their turtle shells.'

For a while they sat in silence. Then Mazar asked, 'How much are a tank and a copter worth, Jim?'

He shrugged.

'Devil knows . . . Many millions.'

'Then Brezhnev will be spending that much less on American wheat,' said Ali Ghazi.

The guerrillas laughed.

'He's got a hundred thousand mouths to feed just in Afghanistan,' Mazar observed wryly.

'He doesn't have to worry about the Red Army here,' said Ali Ghazi. 'Babrak Karmal is feeding them with beef and lamb. There's hardly a sheep left within fifty miles around the enemy bases.'

The conversation was interrupted by an overhead explosion; fragments of stone showered the little group and the men dived for cover. 'Mortars,' said Ali Ghazi, beckoning his companions into a cave in the rock face.

'What do you want to do with the hay and charcoal, Jim?' asked Mazar.

'Crush the charcoal, mix it with the bales of hay, sprinkle it with petrol and drop the lot on the convoy. There should be enough fuel and ammo on the trucks to take care of the rest.'

'The fire will drive the soldiers into the open,' said Ali Ghazi.

'But what about the tanks?' Mazar asked. 'They won't catch fire from burning hay.'

Jim shrugged. 'Perhaps not, but I wouldn't like to be sitting in a tank with a fire burning round it and getting hotter all the time.'

'It'll be the same with the troop carriers,' Ali added. He chuckled. 'I'd love to know what the Russians will do when they start to fry inside.'

Zafar Ghazi and his men returned, hauling the bales of hay

and six sacks of charcoal. The improvised fire bombs were prepared, ignited and rolled down on to the convoy. The enemy panicked. The tanks and a few troop carriers got away by moving back and forth, squashing the bales and pushing them into the ravine; other carriers and lorries found themselves completely hemmed in. One after another the lorries caught fire. Forced to come out into the open, the fleeing soldiers were decimated. A fuel load exploded, shooting a hundred-foot flame, sprinkling the troop carriers and the still intact transports, and starting a fiery chain-reaction. The Russians scrambled out of their armoured vehicles and fell by the dozen as they slithered down the steep slope to the river. An ammunition truck exploded and swept a stretch of the road clean of vehicles and men. The violent blast lifted a forty-ton tank and tossed most of it over the precipice. Stones tumbled from above, hurling men and lorries into the ravine.

Ahmad Mazar got up and shook his fist at the scene of carnage. 'You want to turn Afghanistan red? This is the only kind of *red* you'll ever have here.'

By the time a squadron of copters arrived, spilling troops over the plateau under the protection of screaming MiGs, the *mojahedins* of Ali Ghazi Khan were safely away, climbing a trail to the Khawak Pass.

The enemy razed the long-abandoned village, bombed and strafed the empty plateau and the two caves, then endeavoured to rescue their comrades from the bottom of the ravine, only to lose another copter, blown against a jutting tree by a sudden violent gust of wind.

Ali Ghazi Khan wanted to know how far the rearmost vehicles had withdrawn. Zahor Reza and Muharrem Zarag volunteered to survey the road all the way to Dasht-i-Rewat.

The boys seemed so eager to be of service that Ali Ghazi agreed to let them go, and they set off on mules. Three hours later they returned to report excitedly that there was no enemy unit around Dasht-i-Rewat, except for a solitary Russian tank bearing the number 523, which was resting with a broken track on a twenty-foot roadside slope. Wasting no

46

time, Ghazi sent a runner to fetch Mirza Khel and Abdullah Ghaar, both army deserters and familiar with Russian armoury. He thought the immobilised tank would yield some weapons and ammunition, perhaps the heavy turret machine gun which he longed for. But the wireless set and any fuel they could get would be useful as well.

'If we have enough time, we could dig in the tank and use it as a pillbox to protect the road toward the Khawak,' Mirza Khel ventured and the guerrillas liked the idea until Reza reminded them: 'The tank is lying on a slope with its gun pointing to the sky.'

'Perhaps we can right it,' said Ghaar, and Jim chuckled. 'Forty tons of steel? What do you intend to move it with – mules?'

Ahmad Mazar laughed. He got up and strolled off into a nearby crevasse. When he returned a few minutes later, he was carrying a long, thin object wrapped in oilcloth. Lowering himself on to one knee he put the parcel on a flat slab of rock in front of the Englishman and began to unwrap it.

'Here is something you might like, Jim.' He handed him a marvellously inlaid, silver-worked old shotgun.

Astonished, Jim examined it lovingly. 'A fine old piece, Ahmad . . . A very fine old piece, he said appreciatively. 'And it seems to be in perfect working order.'

'Oh, it works all right,' Mazar assured him. 'You should try it on a Russian.'

The guerrillas laughed.

'I'd prefer some rabbits, or a tin can,' Jim said.

Mazar slapped him on the knee. 'You've just blasted a Russian helicopter, Jim . . . '

'And a tank,' Zafar Ghazi added cheerfully.

Jim shook his head and examined the gun again. He glanced up. 'How much do you want for it, Ahmad?'

Mazar cast him a long, level look and began to scratch his chin. 'How much is it worth?'

'I think I can give you a hundred pounds.'

Mazar pursed his lips. 'Not much for a hundred-year-old gun . . . '

47

'Well – let's say a hundred and twenty.'

The big Afghan burst out laughing. 'Keep it,' he boomed, 'it's yours. It is already paid for.'

'Paid for?'

'By the Russians.' Mazar laughed again. 'One copter and the tank . . . A good bargain.'

'You can store it somewhere at Dahi Baba's cave,' said Ali Ghazi. 'We'll be getting more, and when you've collected enough to send home, we'll help you to carry everything to Peshawar.'

TANK 523

WITH THE hated red star and number 523 marked on its side, the Russian tank was a well-known devil in the small hamlets east of Dasht-i-Rewat; the destroyer of two villages and exterminator of nearly two hundred inhabitants.

Now it lay askew on the roadside slope, its left track ripped off by the primitive mine of an unknown avenger. The crew had been rescued and ferried to the base at Charikar by an armoured copter only minutes before Ahmad Mazar, Mirza Khel, Abdullah Ghaar, and Reza and Muharrem arrived with ten *mojahedins* to take them prisoner. Sheltering nearby, they saw the Russians remove the turret machine gun and crates of ammunition under the protection of the gunship and realised there would be no weapons and cartridges to loot. But the big gun and its shells remained, and shells could be converted into useful explosive devices. As soon as the copter had left, they scrambled towards the wreck.

'Be careful,' Ahmad Mazar warned Mirza Khel and Abdullah. 'The gunship might be coming back for another haul – and it seems odd to me to leave a stranded tank unguarded . . . We'll stay here to cover you, just in case.'

The two men left the sheltering patch of rocky underbrush and walked to the tank. Grasping every handy projection, Mirza Khel clambered to the turret, lifted the hatch and peered in. Raising a hand he signalled 'all clear', then, followed by Abdullah, clambered down inside.

After a few seconds Ghaar's head and shoulders emerged.

'There are two boxes of forty shells left,' he called. 'Nothing else.'

'What sort of shells?' Mazar shouted back.

'Fragmentation.'

'Good . . . I'll send you four men to help unload. Get the radio, too, if you can manage it.'

The four men were about to advance when a distant yell in Pushto startled Mazar. 'Over there!' a *mojahedin* exclaimed. He pointed towards a small incline topped with a pile of stones; an Afghan trooper stood next to it, waving a white cloth. Mazar rose and after a brief exchange three more Karmalists stepped into view, rifles shouldered.

'More deserters,' Ahmad Mazar commented. Taking along a couple of men he joined the soldiers. The one with the cloth was a corporal, by no means just an ordinary deserter. And what the guerrillas had thought was a ruined shepherd's hut was in fact a machine-gun and mortar emplacement.

'We have a present for you,' the corporal told Mazar, and pulled aside a canvas flap. 'The *mojahedins* saw a Red Army sergeant and a pair of soldiers spreadeagled on the ground. Each had a long, triple-edged Russian bayonet through the chest. Commanded by the Red Army sergeant, the group had been left behind to guard the stricken tank.

'A service crane with engineers is already on its way here,' the corporal told Mazar. He and his men had been with the convoy which the *mojahedins* had decimated the day before. 'We lost over three hundred up there,' he complimented Mazar. 'Sixty-five of them Russians.'

'Too few,' Mazar replied gruffly, 'but you've improved on the casualty figures with these three dogs here . . .'

Only then did he offer his hand and embrace the deserters, one after another, like long-lost brothers.

The foursome had had enough of Babrak Karmal and their Soviet 'comrades'.

'The locusts get the best of everything,' the corporal explained, 'they have lamb chops and beef every day, while we get gristly goat meat and scraps . . . You can't even walk off to have a piss without a Russian 'comrade' on your tail. And all leave has been cancelled.'

'Copters!' Muharrem yelled suddenly. 'Over there!' he pointed towards a low line of hills.

'Down!' the corporal snapped and threw a piece of canvas over the dead soldiers. 'The airmen know we're here, don't worry.'

A pair of gunships approached, flying low, barely fifty feet above the short stretch of even ground. They circled the area twice while the soldiers waved friendly hands; then the leading copter clattered away in the direction of Farajghan in the south-east. The other one landed near the road.

Keeping low, Ahmad Mazar surveyed the situation.

'Mirza and Abdullah can't leave the tank now without being spotted.'

The engine of the landed copter stopped but a dull distant rumbling continued and grew louder. Escorted by a tank and a pair of armoured troop carriers, a heavy, tracked salvage crane lumbered towards the site.

'What are you going to do?' the corporal asked Mazar.

'For the moment we can't do anything, except wait and see what happens,' Mazar answered. 'Later on you might be a great help.'

'You can count on us.'

Mazar nodded: 'If the enemy wins – we don't know a thing about your change of sides. We were holding you at gunpoint, understood?'

The corporal nodded. 'Understood. And if you're taken prisoner, we'll help you escape.'

'None of my men will ever fall prisoner,' Mazar said grimly.

Inside the tank Abdullah Ghaar slid to the floor and rolled a cigarette. 'We seem to be trapped,' he said lightly.

'There's half a packet of cigarettes under the seat,' Mirza said, pointing. Abdullah picked it up and pocketed his tobacco pouch. 'S-e-v-e-r-j,' he spelled out the brand. 'Do you want one?'

'We'd better not smoke with the enemy so near,' Miraz warned.

His companion put away the cigarettes. 'You're right. Now what are we going to do?'

Mirza shrugged. 'What Allah wills.'

'I think we might as well take what we can,' Abdullah suggested. Drawing his curving knife he reached for a bundle

51

of wires, but Mirza stopped him. 'Wait! We might still get a chance to escape, tank and all.'

'How?'

'Let them repair the track first. Everything else is working.'

'You want to drive off?'

'And why not? The Russians have no idea about us.'

'Someone might come to inspect the tank.'

'The driver – very likely – but first they'll have to fix the traction.'

Abdullah laughed. 'With a bit of luck we could drive all the way to the Khawak. Can't you see Ali Ghazi's face!'

'We could never cross the Pangar bridge,' Mirza reminded him. Then he added jokingly; 'Perhaps we should drive to Charikar and shoot up the enemy base.'

The roar of heavy engines came closer. Abdullah peered through the gunner's port. 'They're bringing a crane . . . I can see a tank, too.'

'We needn't worry about the tank. It hasn't got any armour-piercing shells either.'

Abdullah reached for a long, green-tipped shell and balancing precariously on the slanted floor bolted it into the breech.

'Just in case the Russians *do* give us a chance to take off,' he said with a grin.

The Russians and a platoon of Afghan troops arrived amidst great clatter and shouts. The service vehicle manoeuvred into position and paid out a length of cable which the sergeant of the engineers hooked into the front tow-bar; then he examined the broken track.

A small group of technicians slithered down the loose slope, followed by two soldiers lugging a narrow crate. They laid out an array of tools on canvas. Chattering among themselves they selected spare parts, bolts and long pins and got down to work, wiping off sweat, gulping water, and cursing the heat and the wild gusts of wind which blew dust into their eyes.

A stocky colonel appeared on the road and stood looking

down, wiping his face and neck over and over again. Through the hatch, Mirza Khel got a good view of him – close enough to have shot him in the belly. It would be great to kill a Russian colonel – still better to catch him alive. 'Perhaps later,' he consoled himself. 'He won't be running away.'

'Sergeant!' the colonel called. 'What's the damage?'

'Nothing serious, sir, but the track is snapped at two places,' the sergeant reported.

'How long will it take to fix it?'

'Half an hour or so, Comrade Colonel.'

'Good,' said the colonel. 'Hurry up.'

He lit a cigarette and lowered himself on a slab of rock. He watched the working party for a while, then turned and shouted something, and a soldier brought across an expensive stereo radio-recorder. The colonel turned it on to blare taped Russian music.

'He got himself a Hitachi in the bazaar of Kabul or Herat,' Mirza grumbled. The Russians enjoyed shopping in the bazaars, usually flanked by a dozen of Karmal's traitors – they would never go unescorted. Ahmad Mazar, who used to live close to the Soviet border, had told his companion about the first days of the invasion. In the townships of Mazar-i-Sharif, Balkh, Tashkurgan and Haibak and wherever the Soviet convoys halted, the shops were virtually stripped of western goods. The Red Army had plenty of ready cash when they moved in – 'Afghan money printed in Russia,' as Ali Ghazi Khan had remarked.

Voices, orders, shouts . . .

The engine of the crane roared into life; the cables tightened, the front of the tank moved and lifted a little.

'*Stoy!*' the sergeant yelled. The crane stopped. '*Davai!*' he urged his men, giving a hand himself. 'Move!'

Bolts were hammered out and nuts unscrewed; one by one the damaged sections were replaced. The colonel's radio blared:

'The Cossack generals are all beaten,

They run from the field far and wide . . . '

Abdullah couldn't take his eyes off the colonel.

'He's having a party,' he whispered to Mirza, as two more

officers joined the colonel. Sandwiches and bottles of beer were served by a pair of soldiers, and the officers unbuttoned their jackets. 'It's so hot,' the colonel grunted, then called to the sergeant and tossed over a couple of bottles.

The sergeant called back his thanks and there was a brief pause while the engineers drank.

'Get down! Mirza hissed as one of the Russians came and peered through the gunner's hatch. Thinking how funny it would be to shoot him between the eyes, Abdullah dropped.

The face vanished. The engineers went back to work, and at last the sergeant reported: 'We're ready, Comrade Colonel.'

The front was lowered, the cable detached, and the crane withdrew a dozen yards or so. The colonel turned off his Hitachi and rose. 'Let's go . . . ' He ordered the sergeant to drive back on to the road.

The sergeant climbed to the turret. Ghaar grasped Mirza's arm. 'He's coming inside,' he whispered tensely and the two men crouched in a corner. The hatch was flung open and the Russian peered in. Satisfied, he turned and clambered down the iron footholds – and froze terrified – as Abdullah's hand clamped over his mouth and a long curving knife was pressed against his throat. Mirza snatched his pistol, and Abdullah shoved him into the driver's seat.

'Move!' he snarled, brandishing the knife. *'Move!'* Pale and shaking, the sergeant swallowed convulsively, but turned on the engine. Mirza closed the turret-hatch. The tank lurched forward and rumbled on to the road; the enemy troops cheered. The sergeant cast a terrified glance at his captors. 'Keep going,' Mirza said coldly.

'Where to?' the sergeant choked.

'Straight on into the copter.'

Out on the road the colonel shouted something and began gesticulating wildly. Russians and Karmalists gathered round him, watching the salvaged tank roll across the road and into the stone-strewn field, but no one yet suspected trouble. Perhaps the sergeant was only testing the controls and would turn back in a minute. But the tank rolled on, and its gun turned and pointed towards the road. Sitting round the launching pads the startled copter crews scrambled to their feet, yelled a garbled warning and scattered. An instant later, Tank 523 smashed into the gunship and mangled it into a lump of twisted metal. Mirza fired the gun, hoping to hit the wheels of the tank, but he aimed too high and the shell blasted the service vehicle, which overturned. The crane crashed down on a troop carrier and put it out of action. Mirza loaded another shell and fired instantly, raking a bloody trail through the scattering troops. He saw the colonel roll into the ditch, but could not tell whether he was dead or only wounded.

'The gunsight must be too high.' The realisation flashed through his mind as he loaded again.

'Forward!' Abdullah Ghaar yelled, and prodded the driver in the ribs with his knife. The engine howled and the tank picked up speed. Another tank opened up, hurling a funnel of smoke, gravel and dust twenty feet into the air.

'To the left!' Mirza commanded. Rolling and pitching like a ship in heavy seas, the tank raced towards the low hill where Mazar and the four deserters were sheltered. At once, Ahmad Mazar realised what Mirza and Abdullah were doing and the *mojahedins* opened fire against the exposed enemy. The Karmalist corporal joined in with the heavy machine gun, and his men began to lob mortar shells on the road. Mirza worked the gun like one possessed and this time managed to land a shell right in front of the Russian tank. It stopped, but fired back.

'Svolech!' Mazar swore at the enemy in Russian and raced towards the road with his men close behind. The guerrillas spread out. The troop carrier fired a few machine-gun salvoes, then reversed and tried to flee, but it had barely rolled a hundred yards when Mirza's shell caught it between the wheels. The *mojahedins* arrived on the road and charged the sheltering survivors like a band of madmen, fighting with bayonets, riflebutts, and knives, and kicking frantically. Six guerrillas charged the tank, three on either side, until it dawned on Mazar that the Russians were all dead and the surviving Karmalists were throwing away their weapons. He still had eight men, including the boy Reza. 'Stay down!' he yelled, pushing the boy into a hollow. He saw the Russian gunner hit the commandeered tank and shatter its wheels, but the armour appeared intact: Mirza and Abdullah had probably survived the blast. The enemy tank tried to back away from the charging guerrillas. Its turret hatch flung open and a soldier sprang to the heavy machine gun; an instant later a grenade exploded on the turret, blowing man and gun to smithereens. A hundred yards away, Abdullah Ghaar and Mirza Khel jumped from the useless tank and ran headlong into the last shell fired by the Russian gunner. Both men vanished in the funnel of fire and smoke.

Mazar and another man were already on the rear armour. 'Watch out!' he shouted, and found himself staring into Reza's blood-stained face. What was the boy doing on top of the enemy tank? He tore the pin of his grenade, dropped it through the hatch, then dived for Reza and swept him to the ground.

A muffled blast. Fire and smoke billowed from the turret. The tank stopped. With Reza still lying underneath him, Ahmad Mazar grunted, 'I told you to stay low. Now look what's happened.' Anxiously he looked for the wound in Reza's hair. The boy grinned. 'It's only a cut,' he said, obviously proud of his spilled blood. But there was an ugly red stripe of raw skin across his skull.

'What did you want to do anyway? You haven't got any grenades.'

The rest of the *mojahedins* joined them, with the four deserters. 'How many have we got left,' asked Mazar.

'Five – not counting the corporal and his men,' one of the survivors answered.

'And the enemy?'

'There are a couple of wounded Russians near the road.'

'Shoot them!' Mazar growled. He turned to the corporal.

'Do you have a first-aid kit?'

'Yes.'

'Then take care of the boy's wound.'

Reza went off with the corporal. Near the road two shots rang out, and a couple of *mojahedins* came back. 'The colonel is dead, too, but we got his stereo set,' one of them reported triumphantly.

'Go and take what you want,' said Mazar and the guerrillas dispersed to search the bodies for valuables. Only the three deserters remained. 'Go and take your share,' Mazar told them, 'you deserve it.'

He walked slowly over to the spot where Mirza Khel and Abdullah Ghaar had fallen. All he could find were a great hole in the ground and shreds of clothing. Pieces of flesh clung to them.

Young Reza joined him, bandaged and carrying a sub-machine gun. 'What's going to happen to the prisoners?' he asked warily, gesturing toward the sullen group of captured Karmalists.

'They're going to carry our booty all the way to the Khawak. We've only got a few mules.'

Reza gave a sign of relief. 'I thought you wanted to shoot them too,' he blurted out. Mazar shook his head and smiled. 'We would never shoot an Afghan unless he betrayed a *mojahedin*,' he said.

PARAKIN

SAFAK PARAKIN, twenty-two, came from Soviet Turkmenistan and served in a transport regiment stationed at Jalalabad. He was one of the first Moslem Red Army soldiers sent to Afghanistan shortly after the invasion, when the Politburo still considered it a good idea to dispatch a number of Moslems with the occupying forces. Like his comrades, Parakin had come to Afghanistan 'to assist the free Afghans in their just struggle against the Western imperialists and expansionist China'.

It would not be long before the Politburo changed its policy of 'Islamic brotherhood': there were too many Turkmens going to join the rebels, with all the equipment they could carry. After seven months of experimenting, Moscow replaced them with Fresh troops from Central Siberia and the Ural districts.

From his earlier days in Afghanistan, soldier Safak Parakin felt confused and in a sense cheated. Throughout his life religion had been anathema at home and, as with all other beliefs, Islamic traditions were suppressed and ridiculed. There was no religious education in Soviet Turkmenistan. The village *mullahs* and *hojas* – the religious teachers – had been expatriated, settled in distant regions of Siberia or thrown into labour camps with other reactionaries and 'enemies of the people'. The mosques had been converted into 'houses of culture', storerooms, or state farm machine sheds. Korans, printed in Iran, Pakistan and Afghanistan were available only on the black market, at exorbitant prices. A hundred roubles for a smuggled Koran was quite common, and only communities could afford to buy one. The observance of Islamic holidays and religious ceremonies was discouraged, or prohibited outright. Even the annual fasting of Ramadan was considered decadent and anti-socialist behaviour. Devout Moslems, who practised the customary sacrifice of sheep after the fasting, were compelled to apply for a permit to slaughter livestock, and in most cases were refused. Those who observed the *Kurban bayram* without a permit were liable to prosecution.

After the invasion of Afghanistan the official line suddenly changed. The Agitprop department of the Party in Turkmenistan issued new guidelines, and the newspapers began printing wonderful stories about Moslem communities thriving and prospering in the USSR. Village mosques, especially those close to the border, were cleaned, whitewashed and opened for religious service. Brand new Korans came from Moscow and Leningrad for free distribution and Islamic schools opened for the first time since the Revolution. The *mullahs* and *hojas* were brought back by special transport, reinstated as religious leaders, and told by the Party to call from the minarets five times a day and forget where they had spent the last five or ten years.

In Chabek, a small town on the Amurdarja river, only two miles from the Afghan border, the repatriated *imam* were addressed by the local Party secretary.

'We are giving you a chance to repent and become useful Soviet citizens again,' he told them. 'We want them to hear you calling all the way to Kabul.'

The people were encouraged to observe their religious days and during the annual fasting the industrial establishments now kindly assigned their Moslem workers to night shifts, so that they could eat while working. When everything had been neatly arranged, busloads of Afghans from Kabul and Herat, Arab students studying in the USSR and diplomats from the Middle East, were brought to Turkmenistan on conducted tours to see with their own eyes how well their Moslem brothers lived in the Soviet Union. During this unusual tourist activity the local shops were stuffed with goods never seen there before and printed texts from the Koran appeared in the windows of Moslem houses.

By the time they'd finished, it looked as if it wasn't Russia who had invaded Afghanistan, but that Islam was conquering the USSR.

In the Red Army units stationed in Afghanistan, the political officers began to speak of the 'Islamic brotherhood' between Afghan and Russian Moslems, 'which should be fostered and deepened for mutual benefit'. Entire regiments of Moslem troops were issued with extra rations for the sole purpose of distributing goodies to the friendly locals, with whom the soldiers had been encouraged to fraternise. 'Go to the mosque and join in the prayers,' Parakin's political officer advised his regiment. 'You know it's only gobbledygook, but the Afghans will be pleased and your presence will enhance the image of the Red Army.'

Neither Safak Parakin, nor the majority of his companions was blinded by this sudden change of attitude. Russian political strategy had always been flexible, able to adapt to new, favourable situations. Parakin still remembered a lecture in which his political officer had explained: 'When there is a conflict between a capitalist and a socialist system – however reactionary, or deviationist that socialist system may be – the USSR will always support the latter one. When there is a conflict between two capitalist, reactionary, or even fascist systems, we must support the lesser developed one, whose working class will be more receptive to ideological influence. And the Soviet Union will assist every Communist-oriented movement, peaceful or armed, in every capitalist country, even if the aims and methods of those movements do not confirm with our views. They may be deviationists, or revisionists, but such leftist movements are struggling to over-throw a capitalist system of government. Once they are in power, the revisionist elements can be eliminated and the power handed over to genuine Marxist-Leninist comrades.'

Safak Parakin also remembered some political seminars given when he was a member of the local *Komsomol,* the youth organisation of the Party. The Khmer Rouge of Cambodia were 'brave and resolute Communist comrades', until the Vietnamese moved in and China took the Cambodian side. Soon afterwards the 'comrades' became 'armed reactionary bands in the service of the Chinese revisionists'.

When the Shah of Iran fled and Ayatollah Khomeini seized power to unleash the greatest bloodshed in Iranian history, the Soviet press said little. When the American diplomats were taken hostage, Parakin's political officer called the United States 'a tottering giant populaced by fat capitalists without will or muscle – just pot-bellies, with cigars in the mouth and piles.'

'How long, Comrades,' he asked, 'do you think the Teheran rabble would manage to occupy the Soviet Embassy? For six hours – the time it would take for our tanks to reach Teheran. The capitalists are weak and doomed and anyone can kick them up the arse. But no one can kick the USSR without receiving a good kick in return. This is why our friends all over the world have faith in us – because we never let them down.'

There had been a great deal of discussion in the political seminars about the imperialist plot to seize Afghanistan and instal nuclear missiles there against the USSR; about how CIA agents and Pakistani Army officers were training rebels, inspiring them to overthrow the legitimate government. When Parakin arrived in Afghanistan, he was quite prepared to fight against American paratroopers and Pakistani commandos and so were his companions. Instead, they found themselves shelling and machine-gunning primitive villages like the ones the Russian *muzhiks* – the landless serfs – had lived in before the Revolution. Parakin saw jets and helicopter gunships bomb and strafe village mosques during the 'abdes' prayer time, when the local men – all considered potential rebels – were assembled in a restricted space and could be slaughtered 'economically' without wasting ammunition. The next best targets were wedding parties and funeral processions.

Safak Parakin met no American paratroopers, or Pakistani commandos. Acting under orders, but also following his own feelings, he tried to make friends with a few Afghan Moslems – they had quite a number of Turkish words in common from both languages. But whenever he tried to convince the people that the Red Army had come to help them, he was met with stony, sceptical eyes and sarcastic remarks.

'If you really want to help us, Safak, you can easily do so,' said one of his Afghan friends. 'Just hand over your gun and cartridges.'

'I'd be shot for that,' Parakin objected, thinking the man was only joking.

'Not if you came over to our side,' the Afghans told him. 'We have little to offer, but you can live the life of a free man.'

'Are you asking me to fight against my own people?' Parakin realised that his hosts were quite serious.

An elderly *imam* said calmly, 'You wouldn't be fighting your own people, but their oppressors. The Russians are not your people – not through race or tradition.'

Parakin simply shook his head. 'I could never shoot at my former comrades,' he said gravely, 'however just your cause may be.'

'No one will ask you to shoot,' said a stocky, bearded, round-faced Afghan, obviously much respected by his companions. 'But you could teach our *mojahedins* how to fight better, or just go to Pakistan.'

'I wouldn't be much help to you if I went to Pakistan.'

'There would be one enemy soldier less for us to fight against and perhaps kill . . . '

'Do you consider me an enemy?'

'Not you, Safak – only your uniform.'

There was a long pause. Then Safak said bitterly; 'The Party would take revenge on my family.'

'Not if you died a hero's death,' came the surprising reply.

Parakin did not understand the significance of this lost proposition until the day he came back to his Afghan friends with his Kalachnikov automatic rifle, a pair of pistols, eight handgrenades and a bag of ammunition.

He was given a most cordial reception.

'Who are you?' he asked the round-faced, stocky man he had been talking to on several occasions.

'My name is Ali Ghazi,' the man said, smiling. 'I have a small group of freedom fighters in the Anjuman range.'

And Parakin suddenly realised that throughout the weeks of friendly fraternising, he had not been entertained but subtly interrogated about the deployment of Soviet troops and their equipment. It also occurred to him that, even without deserting, he had already revealed enough military secrets to face the firing squad.

The Afghans smuggled him, wearing native clothes and riding a mule, to Dahi Baba's camp in the Anjuman, a number of large caves in a precipitous rock face, which was safe from intrusion from air or land. Parakin's uniform and papers – full of bullet holes and sprinkled with his own blood – were dumped in front of the police station in Charikar with a note attached. 'Another Russian invader has met his deserved fate. Death to the infidels.'

Safak Parakin embarked on his new, strange, free life. And when he expressed his concern about his family being notified of his death, Dahi Baba reassured him. 'We have many friends across the border, Safak. Ali Ghazi Khan will find a way to tell your family the truth and advise them to keep quiet.'

Parakin liked Dahi Baba from the moment they met. He was about sixty, a former smith and motor mechanic in Jalalabad with a prosperous workshop. When the Russians moved in he gathered his four assistants and all the tools they could carry and moved into the mountains to help the *mojahedins*. The guerrillas of the Khawak Pass had set him up in the safe caves, accessible only by a single trail, and there he started a new workshop to repair weapons and manufacture new ones and explosive devices. Gradually more skilled men joined him, among them Musa Gawar, a former Kabul engineer, and Muharrem Kunduz, a student of chemistry, who had spent two years studying in the USSR and spoke good Russian. Bazi Noor, Ali Jamrad and Aftab Ahmad, a gunsmith from Peshawar, were just some of Dahi Baba's helpers. Carrying an array of tools in their wide belts, they would go into action whenever an enemy tank, armoured car or lorry broke down and was stranded in the nearby hills.

They removed anything which might come in useful: guns, grenades, shells, radio sets, batteries, generators and petrol.

Guerrillas from far and wide came to Dahi Baba with broken gun barrels, parts, tools – eager to have their weapons fixed, or learn how to repair them themselves. Dahi Baba even made mortars, gauged to accommodate captured Russian artillery shells which he fitted with fins. The shells could be launched from their own castings with a reduced charge, or simply be tossed by hand from a high cliff on to the enemy advancing on the road below.

Dahi Baba was a small, lean, bow-legged man with a bushy white beard, hair and eyebrows, whose cheerful disposition made him many friends, even important men from Pakistan. One such individual was Zebak Vahan, nicknamed by the guerrillas, 'Genghis Khan' – not only on account of his distant Mongol ancestry, but because of his incredible skill in stealing and hoarding a vast assortment of Russian military hardware.

Commanding six hundred warriors, Zebak lived in the 'horn' in the province of Wakhan: the narrow strip of land stretching all the way to the Chinese border between Soviet Tadzhikistan, India and Pakistan.

Vahan lived in Kila Panja, three miles from the Soviet border. When the Red Army crossed the Ab-i-Panja river to occupy the province, Zebak, his brothers, and all their relatives fled to Lunkho, in the Katch Pass, in Pakistani territory.

Having been a smuggler in all his life, Zebak was familiar with every trail, ravine, cave and peak in the area, and gave the Russians so much hell that in the end the local commander decided to satisfy himself with the road and the villages along it close to the border. Tanks trying to patrol the wilderness were blown up. Troops sent to search for the rebels never returned. The helicopter gunships found nothing to attack on the rock-strewn hills, hidden in mist almost every morning. Yet, like ghosts, the riders of Zebak Vahan would charge out of the snow, demolish an enemy installation, kill a few dozen invaders, and vanish without trace. The Asian troops of the

Red Army were a superstitious lot, and in the end the Soviet commander had to dig in the tanks to use as pillboxes along the only road, while the 'horn' belonged to Vahan and his riders.

According to Ali Ghazi, Zebak was the only guerrilla leader who never lacked weapons or ammunition. He even had four Chinese field guns, whose three-inch shells packed enough power to damage tanks two miles away.

Wang Chen Yuang, the commander of the Chinese border guard in the Wakhjir Pass in Sinkiang, was an old 'associate' of Zebak and the Chinese were always ready to furnish him with weapons and ammunition, not only because Zebak would use them against the hated Russians, but because he paid for everything in gold and silver.

Only Zebak Vahan and his brothers knew the source of their fabulous means of exchange.

Safak Parakin tried to make himself useful. He drew sketches of the Soviet installations he was familiar with and helped to plan the safest way of attacking them. He gave lectures to the *mojahedins* on how to fight the superior enemy and survive in the process. With Dahi Baba's assistance he made plywood and cardboard models of every type of armoured vehicle the Red Army had in Afghanistan in order to give Ali Ghazi's men some practical training in attacking tanks and troop carriers with relative safety, staying in the 'blind spots' and alleys where the enemy machine-gun fire could not reach them. He taught the guerrillas where to place explosive charges and grenades and where to aim with the bazooka. In his spare time he wrote leaflets addressed to his former comrades, revealing the true nature of the Soviet adventure in Afghanistan. The leaflets were duplicated and scattered around the Russian bases and housing complexes.

One evening the customary dinner conversation turned to the grave problems presented by the helicopter gunships, which could hunt, destroy and kill virtually unopposed. Safak Parakin asked if it wasn't possible to get some rapid-fire AA-guns from Pakistan. Glumly Ali Ghazi explained that while the Pakistanis were very sympathetic to the Afghan cause, treated the refugees well and were willing to overlook small arms and ammunition purchases in Peshawar and elsewhere, Islamabad was extremely reluctant to provide sophisticated weapons and risk openly antagonising the Soviets.

'It's not that the government is worried about a possible Russian invasion of Pakistan,' Ali Ghazi explained. 'Moscow knows perfectly well that if the Red Army crossed the border it would probably trigger a far greater war. But the Russians can easily retaliate 'by proxy' – they can inspire their faithful supporter Indira Gandhi to stir up trouble in Kashmir, as they did in Angola, using Fidel Castro.'

Jim did not agree with him. 'As a matter of fact I'm fairly certain that India's soft stand on the Afghan problem is actually restraining the Kremlin and in a sense even protecting Pakistan,' he said. 'The Russians cannot afford to lose their only powerful friends in the area, and they probably would if they attacked Pakistan.'

'Allah knows,' Ali Ghazi said thoughtfully, 'I wish you were right, Jim.'

'Why won't you try Zebak Vahan's Chinese connection?' Jim suggested. 'The Chinese aren't scared of offending the Soviets.'

'We've thought of that – but to deal with Vahan, not to mention the Chinese in Sinkiang, you need gold and silver . . .'

Whereupon the Englishman promptly suggested that a patriotic donation of gold and silver by the people of the free village should easily resolve the problem.

'Your womenfolk have more gold than the Bank of England,' he teased. 'Think of all those bracelets, and the gold coins they're laden with, Ali – I've seen some of your brides wearing a pound of gold on each arm. If every family offered only one coin or bracelet you could buy a gun.'

The *mojahedins* thought this over, and a lively discussion began. Ahmad Mazar supported Jim's idea wholeheartedly, but some of them insisted that the women shouldn't be deprived of their wedding gifts. Then Ali Ghazi said gravely:

66

'We offer our blood every day for freedom. Our women can't refuse to sacrifice a few jewels for the sake of our country.'

'That's right,' Zafar backed up his brother. 'Unless we have good weapons people will be sacrificing much more than a few jewels.'

'Their villages, children, livestock,' said Mazar gravely. 'Their future . . . '

The next morning Ali Ghazi sent his brother, Ahmad Mazar, and the engineer Musa Gawar with ten riders to visit the villages of Nuristan and Badakshan, to talk to the *mullahs* and *hojas* and get their help. 'If Allah wills, you'll come back with the gold for the guns,' said Zafar Ghazi.

They set off and returned almost two weeks later, grinning from ear to ear. They brought with them almost a hundred-weight of gold and silver. When everything had been sorted and examined, Ali Ghazi said happily: 'We've got about thirty-five pounds of gold.'

'Which should make some twenty-eight pounds of pure gold,' added Jim, surveying the heaps of bracelets, rings and coins – old and new ones: Iranian Rials, Turkish Reshats, British, Indian, Pakistani coins and even French Marengos.

'Your idea worked,' Mazar boomed.

'My ideas always work,' Jim said with a grin, and recoiled from Mazar's brotherly slap on the shoulder, which had an affectionate force of a sledge hammer. The *mojahedins* laughed. 'I'm still sore from the last one,' Jim said.

'Do you think we have enough gold to buy a rapid-fire gun and ammunition?' Ali Ghazi asked.

'No doubt about it,' Jim replied. 'It's quite a handsome pile – and you've got some silver as well.'

Later that evening Ali Ghazi Khan chose a group of riders to go on a purchasing expedition under the command of Zafar and Ahmad Mazar. Safak Parakin, who was acquainted with artillery weapons, volunteered to go along too, and Ali Ghazi agreed. 'Come back with a good gun and as many shells as you can carry,' he told the young Russian.

'It might change the whole course of the war round the Khawak Pass.'

The relatively safe route which the party was to follow cut across the Chitral region of Northern Pakistan to Zebak Vahan's camp somewhere in the Katch Pass. Ali Ghazi hoped that Vahan would help his brother and Mazar on the second lap of the long haul across the Soviet occupied 'horn' to the Chinese frontier and back, a perilous four-hundred-mile trip.

Having noticed the absence of two riders who had gone with Zafar to collect gold, Ghazi asked his brother what had happened to them.

'They tried to steal a couple of rings and bracelets,' Zafar Ghazi replied quietly, 'and we gave them what they deserved.' And he tapped the stock of his automatic rifle.

THE GUN FROM SINKIANG

ZAFAR GHAZI did not find Zebak Vahan near the Lunkho peak in the Katch Pass. It was only at Amunat, beneath the towering range of Istrag, that he learned that Zebak was camping forty miles to the east, on the Pakistani side of Baroghil. This was the only other negotiable pass between Pakistan and Wakhan province: the Afghan 'horn' bordering four countries: the USSR, China, India and Pakistan.

Ghazi's lack of proper information caused a hundred-mile detour, for he found no passable trail between the Katch and Baroghil. His frustrated party had to double back all the way to Kila Drasan, take the path to Mastui, then once again ride northwards, along the winding Pangkora stream. They were set back by six days, and winter was already blowing frosty winds and snowdrifts across the sparsely forested heights.

The ride was excruciating even for the hardy mountaineers of Nuristan, accustomed to the icy trails of inhospitable heights; the mountains they had to negotiate now were some of the largest in the world. At 24,000 feet, Tirich Mir dominated the whole region. Istrag, Lunkho and the Baroghil were only a few hundred feet lower, and nowhere did the weary travellers descend below fifteen thousand feet. The icy winds and lack of oxygen taxed not only the men but their mounts and pack mules, and frequent rests were necessary to keep the beasts on their feet.

Fortunately, the local guides knew the area well. Making good use of every passable short cut, they moved from crest to crest, from shelter to shelter and from one remote hamlet to another where roof, fire, food and fodder could be found and chilled bones warmed for the next onslaught.

At last they found Zebak's camp, a few miles below the Pass on the Pakistani side of the frontier. To Ghazi's pleasant surprise the site was a permanent one with solid stone huts and sturdy yurts, their frames securely fastened to withstand the strong winds and covered with hides and felt. It was a large camp, sheltered by three nearby caves in the cliffs, which accommodated not only Zebak's six hundred guerrillas, but their families as well.

There was a pair of stone pillboxes with machine guns and three-inch field guns facing the slope up the Pass; as Zebak later explained, 'Just in case the infidel dogs of Brezhnev should decide to make a sweep into Pakistan.'

He and his brothers received the weary riders from Nuristan most cordially. The famous 'Genghis Khan' of the 'horn' was a big, authoritative, craggy man with distinctly Mongol features. He had a deep, booming voice, a robust sense of humour and ample self-confidence. His hatred of the invaders knew no bounds; he would seldom even refer to them as Russians – they were infidel dogs, pig-eaters. Bearded and turbanned, with his long, drooping moustache, Zebak was more like a medieval warrior prince than a twentieth-century rebel leader. His horse was caparisoned in silver; and silver decorated the butts of his automatic rifle, revolver, his dagger and long knife, curved like a Nepalese kukri.

'We are safe here,' he reassured Ghazi and Mazar and they rested in front of a roaring fire, eating roast lamb and sipping tea. 'They tried to raid us only once – came over the Pass and we blasted them into the ravine. Our Pakistani friends turned a blind eye – we defend their border and they can sit comfortably in Mastui and concentrate on the Indians . . . The pig-eaters are still down there, about eighty of them, frozen solid. Perhaps a few learned professors will be thrilled by their discovery in a thousand years time. Now their commander knows better. He would seldom move from Kila Panja, my village, where he feels more secure, comfortably close to the border . . . The dogs daren't even use the road along the Ab-i-Panja, except at twilight.'

He paused, looked at Zafar Ghazi and Ahmad Mazar, then asked Parakin, 'What do the Moslems across the border think?'

'The same as you do, Zebak Khan,' Parakin replied

quietly, 'the ordinary working people, that is. The party secretaries, generals and soldiers come from Bielorussia, or Leningrad; the Turkmen conscripts in the Red Army are sent far from home, to Kiev, or to Archangelsk.'

'The day will come when we liberate and unite all Moslems.'

'Insallah,' said Parakin. 'God's will be done.'

Zebak's dark eyes shifted to Zafar Ghazi.

'So, you came to buy a rapid-fire gun and ammunition from the Chinese, and you have the gold to pay for it . . . '

'Thirty pounds of gold, melted into ingots,' Zafar told him. 'We also have two hundred and twenty coins from England, India, Pakistan, Iran and Syria.'

He reached into his bag and withdrew an ingot. He handed it over to Zebak who weighed it expertly in his hand. He bit his underlip, and gave Ghazi a long, level look and asked slyly, 'You haven't added anything else to it, have you?'

'Dahi Baba is your friend . . . '

There was a pause.

'Yes, we've known each other for almost thirty years,' Zebak Vahan conceded. 'He wouldn't cheat me.'

'That gold is from bracelets, rings, necklaces and earrings – it was all given by the villagers.'

Zebak seemed surprised. 'Did they really give you so much gold of their own account? What did you tell them?'

'The truth.'

Zebak moved his head in the local manner of approval.

'Then you should have about twenty-five pounds of pure gold . . . It should be enough for a good gun and five hundred rounds.'

'How much is an AA-gun worth?' Mazar broke in. Zebak shrugged. 'I don't know. We never bought any.'

'Do you think the Chinese would sell?' asked Parakin.

Zebak chuckled. 'The Chinese I know would sell you the Great Wall if you had enough gold to pay for it . . . ' He turned back to Ghazi. 'We shall have to talk with Colonel Wang Chen.'

Parakin, still pondering, broke in again.

71

'But how could Colonel Wang sell a big gun that must be on his inventory?'

Zebak laughed. 'It's very simple. Wang sells you a gun, pockets his profit then buys another from a commander somewhere in Sinkiang, who in turn buys one from Sechwan. The commander in Sechwan reports the loss of a gun in a towing incident, or blown up during exercise – a manufacturing fault, and gets a replacement from Peking free of charge . . . The whole Chinese Army is a huge commercial venture. You might not believe it, but you can buy anything there, even an aeroplane – lost on a training flight . . . Just take enough gold, or good money. Now – ' He turned to Ghazi. 'How do you want to carry the gun back to Nuristan?'

'The way we came . . . Along the Chitral and the Dorah pass.'

'You'll have to dismantle it completely.'

Zafar shook his head. 'No, we will carry it ready to fire, perhaps on a sled. The Russians might discover what we are transporting and try to stop us.'

'Not in my lands,' Zebak said firmly. 'We have them well trained – like good dogs – but the Pakistanis might object.'

'They'll look the other way.'

'For how much?'

'Fifty gold coins – so far,' said Ghazi. 'It might cost you another fifty on the way back.'

'We'll keep that much in reserved. I am only worried about the last leg to Nuristan. There are always some copters out hunting.'

'Well, shoot them down,' Zebak replied flatly.

The next morning Zebak Vahan, his youngest brother Zagor and eighty riders joined Ghazi's caravan of thirty. They crossed the Pass and rode off towards the Chinese frontier at Wakhjir along the southern slopes of the Little Pamir. Safak Parakin wondered why Zebak was travelling with such a large party – they could not possibly remain unobserved. The craggy smuggler-turned-*mojahedin* told him with a laugh,

'Because I want your infidel brothers to see us on the move and lose a good night's sleep wondering what we're up to.'

On the map, thirty miles a day did not seem like much, but converted into practical travelling it was brutal. On the third day the caravan ran into a blizzard. The wind howled along the great cliffsides they passed under, and whirling snow-flakes blinded men and animals. At a jutting overhang, Zebak ordered a halt. The men cleared a patch of ground and heaped the snow high to provide a crude wall, blocking out some of the wind. Then they lit a dozen fires and camped down for the rest of the day and the following night.

Colonel Wang Chen, Commander of the Chinese regiment stationed near the Wakhjir Pass, received Zebak and his brother with a broad smile, and a great many warm hand-shakes and back-slappings. He was perhaps fifty, an amiable type, stocky and smiling and with a splendid air of calm. A soldier since the age of fifteen, he was in great sympathy with the Afghan cause.

He put up Zebak and his immediate party in his own spacious log-house and ordered large army tents to be erected for the escort with a hot meal and tea for everyone. When he learned that Safak Parakin was from Russia, he paid special attention to him throughout his three-day stay and treated him particularly well. 'Anyone who is against the Soviets is our friend,' he told Parakin; 'and when a Russian is against the Soviets, he is a brother.' Then he embarked on a lengthy monologue, explaining why the Russians had become the greatest menace to the civilised world, and concluded: 'It wasn't the American capitalists, but the Soviet imperial-ists who opened fire against Chinese fishermen and soldiers at the Ussuri river.*

* On 3 March 1969 a serious clash between Russian and Chinese troops on an island in the Ussuri River on the Russo-Chinese border left 31 Russians and an unknown number of Chinese dead. A second clash occurred on 15 March.

The walls of the colonel's office were covered with large maps, including one of China showing Tibet, an area on the Indian border, Taiwan and a vast region of the far-Eastern USSR shaded and marked: 'Recovered territory', 'Kuomintang Administration' and 'Currently under Soviet occupation'.

The colonel beckoned Parakin to the map of Afghanistan and questioned him in great detail about the Russian troops and armaments stationed there. Parakin answered as best he could, thinking how strange it was to see the same Red Star on caps and helmets, representing the same basic ideals, but implemented with a completely different attitude. 'The Russians always arrive like smiling friends ready to help, but the moment they're inside the house, they start telling you what to do,' said Colonel Wang. 'They came to China, too, in the fifties, to give us weapons and machines, but never any spare parts. When we asked for replacements, they laid down conditions. When some of our leaders or newspapers criticised something they'd done, the turbines of a power plant, or a tank-engine would be delayed for months. In the end we kicked them out and began manufacturing the parts ourselves. China is too great a nation to be dominated by anyone. The world is scared stiff of the Russians, even America, but not the Chinese. Perhaps we are less well equipped, but in the end it is always the manpower that counts. Machines can conquer territory, but only men can hold it.'

Wang spoke calmly and reasonably. 'I was only eighteen when the Party sent me to Korea to fight against the Americans,' he continued. 'My regiment was sent to attack a hill with three thousand Americans on it; they carried the best equipment a soldier can have. We didn't have many good weapons then, so our commander gave what we had to a battalion and sent it to attack the enemy. The battalion was slaughtered before it reached the bottom of the hill. The next wave of two thousand men stormed with old rifles, most of which would not even fire, but the soldiers knew that there were good weapons ahead, waiting to be picked up, and they went a hundred yards further. Some of the third wave didn't

74

even have weapons, but the Americans didn't know that, and they kept firing. Wave after wave followed for three days and three nights. We wouldn't let the enemy relax for a moment. The barrels of the machine guns overheated, and had to be changed, or cooled down . . . You see, after a few thousand shots the machine guns become quite useless. On the third day the enemy soldiers couldn't keep their eyes open – all they could see were Chinese everywhere, even where there weren't any. We lost eighteen thousand soldiers. But we took the hill.'

Wang observed Parakin sombrely. He stretched out his legs towards the fire and went on: 'Brezhnev has twelve thousand tanks poised along our borders and he thinks they could roll all the way to Peking – he knows we haven't got enough anti-tank guns or missiles to stop them – at least not yet. But we know exactly how far a tank can go without refuelling and within that area the enemy wouldn't find a single drop of fuel. We also know how many rounds their guns and machine guns have, how many men it would take to overwhelm a tank and destroy it with grenades and petrol bombs – one hundred and seventy men for each tank to storm it from every direction. Eighty per cent might fall, but the rest would reach the tank and destroy it. We have a million men trained to stop tanks and another million to deal with the supporting infantry.'

There was an intensity of spirit underlying the colonel's words. He was full of confidence in China's power, and not even the grim prospect of a nuclear war scared him.

'Imagine a global nuclear war,' he told his visitors, who were listening intently. 'The large cities and factories will be destroyed everywhere in the world, including those in China. But with the industries ruined, there will be no more ships, warplanes, tanks, missiles or artillery – not even ammunition . . . In China we have tens of millions of people who have not yet seen electric light and who manufacture everything they need from clothes to weapons. They won't perish. And when there are no more bullets left for the rifles, China will still have fifty million men for the last bayonet charge . . . The Russians know this too. We could lose five hundred million people and still be the most densely populated nation in the world.'

Colonel Wang was pleased that China and America were once again on better terms; in the past, they had always been good friends. He only doubted America's ability to establish long-term, firmly set policies to pursue, regardless of outside circumstances.

'We understand that the United States does not wish to destroy China,' he said, smiling, 'and the Americans are surely not afraid of a Chinese invasion . . . And we both know that the Soviets want to conquer the whole world. The USSR is the natural enemy of every free country, a born predator with a perpetual inferiority complex which turned it into a bully. Americans and Chinese could easily become not only good friends, but allies – except for the Nationalist left-over in Taiwan.'

He threw out his arms. 'What is Taiwan compared with China? Is it really worth the friction it causes? Just imagine Brezhnev's face, or the face of whoever comes after him, when the Kremlin receives the news of a full Chinese-American alliance. With American industrial backing we could easily put an army of a hundred million on the field. We could liberate the Soviet-occupied countries, not just in Asia, but in Europe, too, merely by a phone call to Moscow. We could send the Red Army reeling back behind their own borders, like the robbers they are. The Americans insist that they need more and more nuclear missiles because NATO doesn't have sufficient conventional force to stop a sudden Soviet attack . . . What hypocrisy! As if the combined western factories couldn't outproduce the Soviets in every-thing. How long would it take for the NATO countries to manufacture five tanks and warplanes for every one the Russians have? Six months? A year? How many tanks and pieces of artillery could be built for the price of a single ballistic missile? In a year or two they could put a heavy tank every ten yards along the Iron Curtain without invoking the nightmare of a nuclear war. And come to think of it – supported by a thousand Chinese divisions on the other end, there'd be no need to fight in Europe at all. The Russians

would have neither troops, nor arms to threaten people with
. . . ' Wang paused, and sighed. 'But it'll be a long time
before the Americans see the light.'

Sipping tea, Ahmad Mazar jokingly reassured the colonel
that the Afghan people would like nothing better than to see
twenty million Chinese troops charge into Russia – or into
Afghanistan for that matter.

After this lively discussion, Colonel Wang took Zafar Ghazi
aside and told him bluntly. 'We have just the gun you need: it
had twin, three-inch barrels, and fires two hundred and
twenty rounds of high velocity shells converging at twelve
hundred yards . . . You can shoot down anything that flies
with it . . . Come and have a look.'

He led the expectant little group to a large wooden shed
with a guard outside, and showed them a sleek rapid-fire gun
mounted on a wheeled stand.

'It has never fired a round, except in the factory when they
tested it,' he said with a broad grin, and slapped the breech
almost with affection.

'It really is an all-purpose gun,' Safak Parakin told Zafar
Ghazi and Ahmad Mazar. 'You can use high explosive, fragmentation, or armour-piercing shells with it.'

'That's right.' The colonel nodded. 'We have all types of
shells – whichever you prefer.'

'We prefer plenty of everything,' Ghazi replied thoughtfully, studying the gun.

'A good weapon,' Mazar commented.

'Made in China,' Colonel Wang said with pride, 'but the
steel came from England and Germany.' He turned to Ghazi
and Mazar. 'But how do you intend to take it back with
you?'

'We'll try and take it on a sled,' Zafar Ghazi answered,
inspecting the gun appreciatively. It occurred to him that fifty
guns like that distributed around the villages would completely free Nuristan and Kohistan from enemy air attack.
But where were they going to get the money?

He thought vaguely that the lapis-lazuli mines near Kuran

might solve the problem and made a mental note to think about it again. Kuran lay seventy miles north-east of the Khawak. The mines were guarded by the Karmalists and a Red Army detachment with tanks and copters, but the garrison would be isolated and vulnerable in winter.

Colonel Wang's voice brought him back to the present. 'How do you like it?'

Zafar smiled and nodded his approval.

'How much is it worth?'

'I shall discuss that with Zebak . . . How many rounds do you want?'

'As many as you can offer, Colonel,' Zafar replied with a grin, and then corrected himself. 'As many as we can carry.' And Ahmad Mazar added emphatically, 'We won't be able to come back for more shells. Not until after the winter, anyway.'

'We shall see . . .'

Zebak Vahan cut in. 'You must keep in touch with us, and let us know when you're getting low on shells. My men often come here and could pick up a few boxes for you to keep ready at Baroghil.'

'I'll do that. It would be a great help.'

'Saving you half the trip, too.'

Safak Parakin was satisfied as well. The gun was a fine Chinese copy of the Russian original with twin magazines, each holding twenty-two shells, and Colonel Wang was willing to give a crate of vital parts, springs and spare firing mechanism into the bargain. 'We are not like the Russians,' he told Parakin with a broad smile. 'When we give a weapon, we want to see it work.'

The shells were powerful enough to knock out armoured cars and troop carriers and wreck the wheels of a heavy tank.

Drawing Vahan aside, Colonel Wang Chen conducted a brief exchange with him. Then he told Zafar and Mazar: 'Zebak says you have twenty-five pounds of pure gold . . . You can have the gun, a thousand rounds, twenty bazookas with five shells each and fifty Kalachnikov automatic rifles with thirty rounds each.'

'We accept,' Zafar beamed, overwhelmed by the unexpected generosity. Reaching for the colonel's hand he squeezed it happily. 'It is much more than we ever hoped to take back with us.'

'I know. Three hundred shells and the automatic rifles are a gift from China. Fight well.'

Zebak told the men: 'Colonel Wang has decided to forgo his percentage on this particular deal and so have I.'

'But then you've suffered all the hardships of the journey for nothing,' Ghazi blurted out in surprise.

'It wasn't for nothing. I saw my Chinese friends and helped some brother Afghans from Nuristan.'

'And they say you don't really care what kind of government is in Kabul!' said Mazar and Zebak laughed.

'That's true – just as long as it doesn't send too many Customs people into my province. The present one sends pig-eaters, tanks and artillery. So we do have a common cause.'

'I think you are a true patriot Zebak Vahan,' said Mazar with conviction.

'Everyone who kills the infidel dogs is a patriot,' Zebak replied.

At the colonel's command, two Chinese soldiers demonstrated to Ghazi and Mazar how to operate the gun, load and change the magazines, aim and fire; afterwards, Colonel Wang invited Zafar to test-fire a couple of rounds into a cliff, twelve hundred yards away. Ghazi was astonished how easily the twin barrels shifted and the gun turned.

'Now you can say "spakoini noch" – "Goodnight" to the Russian Air Force,' Wang said with a smile.

'Insallah,' Mazar said, 'and it shouldn't be very difficult. They have to fly low and slow in our mountains.'

The next morning the Chinese let fly a large weather balloon to provide Ghazi with a more realistic target. He was still in the seat when a Russian copter showed up on the far side of the border. The nearby Chinese battery began to blaze away, and the copter swung around and fled towards Boza.

Noticing that the Chinese gunners had not been aiming to

hit, Zafar said with some disappointment, 'You could have shot it down.'

'If it had come two hundred yards closer, we should have done,' Colonel Wang replied good-humouredly.

'Still, it would have crashed on Afghan territory,' Zafar pondered aloud and the colonel said, 'True – but on this side of the river, on level ground. We could have towed the wreckage to our side of the border-marker, photographed the lot and stuffed the pictures into Brezhnev's mouth if he opened it too wide.'

Zebak and his party burst into wild guffaws. Parakin was highly amused; he found the colonel and the other officers most amiable, quite unlike the haughty superiors he had known in the Red Army. They behaved informally even among their own soldiers.

In the evening, over a dinner of stewed chicken with rice and green peas, Zafar Ghazi jokingly asked if the colonel wouldn't like to come along and do some fighting in Nuristan. 'I'd come gladly, and bring half a million troops with me,' Wang grinned. 'But,' he threw out his arms, 'the Russians would have to perpetrate a convenient border incident first.'

'Perhaps we can arrange one,' Zebak chuckled, chewing at a chicken leg. 'The next time I come, I'll bring along a few dozen dead Russians, dump them around your camp, then open up on your garrison with blanks. Afterwards you can chase the Russians out of the province.'

Parakin noticed that for the first time, probably in deference to his Chinese friend, Zebak used the term 'Russian' instead of 'infidel dog' or 'pig-eaters'.

With the help of the Chinese soldiers, Ghazi built a low-slung sled for the gun and hitched a team of four horses to it. A pair of loaded magazines were snapped on – 'in case the enemy spots this peculiar-looking load and send a copter to investigate.' The gun was covered with a burlap. The weapons and ammunition were divided between the riders and Parakin understood why Zebak had brought along eighty of them. Ghazi's group alone could never have carried everything across the frozen wilderness.

They were on the road when Parakin said to Zebak: 'I still can't understand how the colonel could give away so much equipment.'

Zebak laughed. 'Despite all their propaganda against capitalism, the Chinese are still good businessmen. They have always been. What do you think Mao Tse-tung used to beat Chang Kai Shek in '49? With the weapons the Americans sent to the Nationalists, half of which ended up on the black market the day after they arrived, and thence straight into Mao's hands . . . Don't tell me they never steal anything in the Red Army.'

'Certainly not weapons and shells.'

'Because there's no buyer. But I know perfectly well that the officers steal meat and other foodstuff from their garrison's ration, and petrol and diesel oil . . . Everything that can be easily accounted for.'

'Anyone who steals over a hundred roubles' worth can be shot,' Parakin said.

'Unless the thief happens to be a district Party secretary, or a member of the local Soviet,' Zebak retorted. 'The Russians are the greatest thieves in the world, Safak. It's a pity you can't see my village – the pig-eaters moved in at four in the morning, and by midday there was not a watch or transistor radio left in the place.'

'Nor a sheep,' added Zagor.

Parakin fell silent.

The caravan followed the course of the Ab-i-Panja river, which was really only a large stream, already partly frozen. Zebak had sent a party of eight men ahead to scout the neighbourhood for enemy patrols. The village of Wakhjir was not occupied by the invaders, but even so only a few hardy families remained. Most of the houses were empty even of furniture which in this godforsaken region consisted mostly of simple bunks and large chests. What the inhabitants could not take along the perilous trail to Pakistan and safety the marauding invaders had stolen.

Zebak Vahan decided to spend the night indoors and since there were enough places for everybody the chilled riders appreciated his decision. They had come only twenty-three

81

miles from the Chinese border, but even a few miles riding in
that frosty, windswept wilderness could drain the strength
from man and beast.

The next morning the temperature had dropped still
further and the sky was overcast. It looked like snow; the
copters would probably remain grounded.

The trail they had followed on the journey out was buried
under fresh snow, but Zebak rode on unhesitatingly, taking
the proper trails and turns like one familiar with every
landmark in the province.

Every now and then trails of mist and drifting banks of fog
closed round them – a welcome cover. Still, a solitary copter
materialised above the lower slopes of the Little Pamir and
came on, clattering low overhead. The caravan dispersed.
The riders dropped into the deep snow just as a salvo of four
rockets streaked towards them and exploded, throwing snow
and chunks of ice into the air. The rockets caused no damage,
but the slugs from a low-slung gun turret killed a horse and
four mules. And then the *mojahedins* opened up with their
Kalachnikovs and the copter rose and withdrew flying
towards Boza.

The caravan resumed its weary trek.

Zafar Ghazi was disturbed by the incident: it suggested that
the Russian commander at Boza knew of the caravan and was
curious enough to dispatch a copter despite the bad weather.
Zebak himself agreed that the copter had not come to attack,
but simply to survey, and had fired only because a lucky
break in the fog presented a chance. His experience told him
to proceed with increased caution, for the infidel dogs might
set a trap further ahead, but he reassured Zafar Ghazi,
anxious for the safety of his gun and ammunition; 'They can
never beat me on the ground in a man-to-man combat, not in
this province. If the pig-eaters plan to attack, I know where
they'll set their trap, and it's still three days ride from here
. . . Relax.'

He was right. For three days the caravan proceeded undisturbed. On the fourth morning Zebak doubled his number of
scouts, now all wearing Russian snowsuits and riding white
horses. He set the distance they should cover, and the caravan

advanced much more slowly. Shortly before noon Zebak stopped, surveyed the distant hills through his binoculars and beckoned Parakin, Ghazi and Mazar to come closer.

'The enemy is over there,' he announced flatly, pointing toward a cluster of distant hills: they were no different from the others, except for a large flock of crows circling overhead. 'The crows,' Zebak explained. 'Where people have eaten they land to pick up the scraps.'

Fifteen minutes later one of the scouts returned on his steaming mount to report the presence of a blocking party landed by copters, five miles before the ascent to the Baroghil Pass.

'There must be a new Commander in Kila Panja,' said Zebak. 'The one I knew would never commit such a stupid blunder. I shall catch them in their own trap.'

Three more riders returned, with more information. The enemy had a dozen machine guns and six mortars. Three copters were parked four-hundred yards behind the planned site of the ambush, two of them covered with burlaps.

Zebak turned to Ghazi. 'Then they don't know anything about your gun.'

He led the caravan half a mile further, then left the trail and cut into the hills, always following the passable path, until they came to a sheltered depression flanked by peaks. 'That one over there should offer a good view of the dogs,' he announced, pointing it out.

'How far away are they?' asked Mazar.

'Five hundred yards – perhaps six hundred, not more.'

He told the men to eat and rest. It was not yet one o'clock, and he didn't want to attack the enemy before dusk; the copters could no longer interfere then. Inviting Ghazi, Mazar and Parakin to accompany him, he set out on foot up the steep slope to survey the situation from the crest. Roped together, the four men clambered up on the icy hillside, hauling more coils of knotted rope to make the descent easier. The climb was tortuous and it took them almost an hour to reach the frozen, windy crest. From there they looked down on the enemy blocking-party and its copters, none more than eight hundred yards away. There were machine-gun positions placed on the mounds, two hundred and fifty yards apart on either side of the trail with six to eight soldiers in each, while a larger position with four machine guns and the mortars lay further ahead.

The plan of the enemy Commander was plain enough. He wanted the caravan to ride into the trap, and would then slaughter it in a crossfire of machine guns and mortars.

'We're a hundred and fifteen against about eighty Russians, but they have machine guns, mortars and copters,' Zafar Ghazi said to Zebak. 'What do you intend to do?'

'I want to haul your gun up here and destroy the copters before we do anything else,' Zebak replied matter-of-factly, and his casual statement startled his companions. It had been hard enough just for them to negotiate the precipice: it seemed inconceivable that a fourteen-hundred-pound gun could ever come up the same way and Safak Parakin did not hesitate to say so.

'Nothing is ever impossible,' Zebak Vahan rebuked him gruffly. 'Two years ago the world said the pig-eaters would pacify Afghanistan in two months. We are still around, holding more territory than the invaders and the traitors in Kabul can call their own . . . To wreck three helicopters and kill eighty infidel dogs, I'd haul that gun up to the Lunkho peak, and that's only five thousand feet lower than Everest.'

Knowing already that nothing and no one could ever deter him, Zafar, Parakin and Mazar went to lend him a hand. He fastened the knotted rope around a hook-shaped boulder and tossed the coil back into the ravine. Using the handholds, three more men climbed up bringing more ropes, all which were anchored, then dropped back down. Within fifteen minutes thirty guerrillas had converged on the peak with automatic rifles, while a team in the cave cut down trees and hacked them into balks that were hauled up to the top.

'We are going to make a winch,' Zebak explained, describing the crude device with which he wanted to lift the gun. He noticed Zafar's worried look and told him cheerfully, 'If we damage it, I'll ride back and bring you a new one out of my own purse.'

'Have you got that much gold on you?' Ghazi taunted, not very convinced.

'I have credit at Wang's place,' Zebak replied with a chuckle. 'We've been doing business together for six years.'

He began his extraordinary task and in an amazingly short time the winch was ready and firmly anchored. Ghazi prayed to Allah it would be strong enough.

Since the far side of the crest presented a fairly even slope down to the trail and the Russian positions, Zebak decided to raise the gun on its sled, suspended obliquely to let the sled 'glide' upward on the precipice without bumping into boulders.

With twenty-four men turning the winch, they hauled the gun to the top and positioned it to look straight down on the enemy flank and the parked copters. Zebak then had a brief discussion with his brother. With fifty riders, Zagor would move towards the Russians, stop short of the trap and engage them frontally, mostly to distract the machine-gun crews. 'The moment the dogs start firing, we'll cut in from above, destroy the copters then eliminate the machine-gun and mortar positions one after another.'

'Insallah,' Zagor remarked, shouldering his rifle. 'Insallah.'

He set off, and Zebak scattered his thirty men between the boulders, close to the slope and with a clear view of the enemy. Taking his seat on the gun platform, Zafar Ghazi centred the foremost copter in the target grid, smiling happily. It would be like shooting a fox at five yards. Mazar and Parakin stood by the loaded magazines.

A layer of fog descended from the Baroghil and drifted towards Sarhad, the enemy-occupied village on the Ab-i-Panja, only eight miles away. Zebak feared that it might envelop the Russians before Zagor had time to make his attack, and he advised Zafar to fire on the copters if the fog threatened to blot them from view. The same idea must have occurred to his brother, for his detachment could soon be seen riding hard towards the trap. The machine gun crews on the mounds along the trail tensed: the eyes of the gunners were glued to the sights. It seemed that the rebels would ride straight into the crossfire, and in his eagerness to win an easy victory the Russian Commander failed to realise that there were far fewer riders than reported and that the pack animals were missing as well.

Inexplicably, Zagor and his *mojahedins* stopped short of the trap, dismounted and scattered, but the startled Russians opened up on them all the same and shot the mounds of snow full of holes. Zagor returned the fire to distract enemy attention from the party on the crest: they could not hit the well-concealed enemy either. The helicopter crews scrambled. The mortars cut in. Soldiers rushed to remove the burlaps from the copters. An instant later Zafar Ghazi hit the one already targeted; it exploded, killing the crew.

Stunned by the sudden disaster, the rest of the airmen and the soldiers scattered, diving for cover behind mounds of snow. Within seconds the two remaining copters were ablaze, then blew up, hurling twisted sheets of fuselage, fragments of plexiglass, propeller blades and components far and wide. The effect of the unexpected shelling from the flank and above was devastating. Orders, coarse yells, curses and cries of agony filtered through the howling wind. The machine-gun crews found themselves under the murderous fire of thirty automatic rifles. Many were hit by the first salvoes: others tried to flee towards less exposed spots and in the centre a platoon of white-clad soldiers surged to the left flank to position themselves against the snipers on the crest.

Saving ammunition, Zafar switched to single shots and began firing into the machine-gun positions.

Along the trail and between the snowy mounds, Zagor's fifty guerrillas rushed forward with blazing guns. Split into two groups, one of them charged round the ambush-site to attack the enemy on the right flank. Confusion turned into panic as the Russians could no longer decide which way to face. Bullets seemed to hit them from every direction.

' "Allah akhbar!" ' Zebak Vahan shouted to Zafar. 'God is great! We have the pig-eaters in the bag.'

'I think I like this gun!' Zafar shouted back over the wind, then winced as a bullet whizzed past his ear.

A sharp explosion, and a fountain of snow and ice fifty

yards behind the gun announced that the mortars were testing the peak. A second blast flung a large boulder down the slope and killed two of Zebak's men. Mazar yelled something which Ghazi could not catch, but he saw him jump, then bend down to recover a three-inch piece of jagged metal which clanked against the undercarriage. It was a close shave – a little higher and it would have taken off Mazar's left leg.

Zafar Ghazi swung the gun towards the Russian mortars and sent their crews crawling behind heaps of snow.

Down below, Zagor's men chased the enemy from one mound to another, turning captured machine guns against those who still resisted.

The fog shifted, and it began to snow. Visibility decreased: the gun and the machine guns could no longer fire with any effect and the skirmish degenerated into a hand-to-hand struggle, then into plain butchery as Zagor's *mojahedins* sought out and killed the hated enemy. Here and there milled small groups of soldiers, outflanked, surrounded and unable to escape. Resistance crumbled; the gunfire petered out, then stopped altogether. From the trail rose a thunderous ' "Allah akhbar!" '

A handful of Russians who tried to flee towards the Ab-i-Panja were mown down by riders in relentless pursuit. The battle was over. Zebak had lost three guerrillas, Zagor eleven and Zafar Ghazi only two because Zebak had wanted the party from Nuristan to remain in the cave and guard the pack mules.

Braking the sled with ropes held by his men struggling on the slippery slope, Zebak had the gun sledded down the peak. At the bottom, he joined Zagor, whose steaming riders were busy rounding up the surviving enemy soldiers. Others ran to collect the scattered weapons and other equipment.

Only twenty-six prisoners were taken, among them a captain, two lieutenants and two sergeants. The Commander, a major from Moscow, had been killed, with another captain. With rifle-butts and vicious kicks and shouting 'Death to the enemy dogs,' the cursing *mojahedins* herded the terrified group into a cave. Pale and shaking the prisoners stared at their captors. Zebak Vahan observed them with eyes full of malice and ordered the delivery of money, watches, rings, cigarettes, lighters, furs and snow-suits, all of which were collected by the guerrillas and deposited on a burlap. Then Zebak halted and singled out a young Russian. 'Come here!' The soldier came forward on unsteady legs. 'Don't shoot, sir!' he pleaded. Zebak burst out laughing. 'You don't use that word at home – there are no "sirs" in the Soviet Union, only serfs.'

'He is a pilot,' Parakin interpreted momentarily forgetting that Vahan spoke good Russian.

'I know, but it makes no difference to us,' Zabak replied. 'The others kill with mortars and machine guns. He kills with rockets and napalm . . . but I'll let this one live.'

'And the others?' Parakin asked miserably.

'You had better not look,' Zebak Vahan answered and Parakin turned and walked away.

Zagor shouted a few harsh, guttural words, and one of the captured machine guns opened up, drowning pleas, cries and curses. In a few seconds it was all over.

The young pilot whom Zebak had spared at random sat crumpled in the snow with his face buried in his hands and his shoulders shaking. Zagor Vahan jerked him to his feet and hissed. 'You can go! Go back to Kila Panja and tell the other infidel dogs about the Vahan brothers and their riders.' Grasping the pilot by the shoulders he spun him round and gave him a vicious kick. 'Move!' Staggering, the pilot fled, falling in the deep snow, scrambling to his feet and running further, glancing back every now and then, expecting to be shot in the back, until fog and dusk swallowed his tottering shape.

'You should always let one live to tell the tale,' Zebak told Ghazi, 'afterwards the other dogs won't be so eager to bite.'

Leaving the sled with the gun where it was, they retired into the sheltered depression in thickly falling snow, preparing themselves for a rough night in the open. Burlaps were stretched between the trees and the guerrillas busied themselves with shovelling up walls of snow to shut out the wind the best they could – for the animals, too. Fires were lit. The men prepared the long overdue meal and made tea. It was impossible to negotiate the Pass in falling snow and darkness.

Zebak and Zagor counted the booty: ten machine guns, forty automatic rifles, eight pistols, 166 hand-grenades, four light mortars and twenty boxes of ammunition. Plus the fur-lined coats, jackets, caps and boots which Zebak immediately distributed among those who needed them during the freezing night. 'You see, we didn't go all the way to China with you for nothing,' Zebak Vahan told Zafar. 'A third of it is going to be yours and two mortars . . . '

'They might come very handy,' Mazar cut in, and thanking him for his generous offer, Zafar Ghazi thought that Zebak Vahan was not nearly as stingy as people made out. 'Our province is a good place to fight in,' Zagor said with a chuckle. 'The Russians and the Chinese give us everything we need.'

'Don't you ever take prisoners?' Parakin asked.

'What would we do with prisoners?' Zagor snorted.

'Perhaps exchange them against some of your captured companions,' Parakin ventured.

Zebak broke in. 'The men I fight with are never taken prisoner,' he said with immense pride. 'They kill, or die fighting like the Japanese . . . Besides, the enemy commanders don't care much about their dogs we capture. As far as they're concerned, the prisoner has failed to do his duty, or is a deserter, a traitor. Once a Russian soldier is in enemy hands, he is no longer trusted by his commander. He might return as a spy of course – you should know that, Safak.'

Early next morning, Zebak sent two men out with the horses to hitch on the gun, and then the caravan set off for the Baroghil Pass in fresh snow, barely advancing a mile an hour. Groups of forty men went ahead, shovelling snow, before the column, and clearing the narrow paths. It was late in the afternoon when they reached the Pakistani side of the Pass and camped down at the abandoned barracks of the Pakistani border-guard. Zebak's camp was only a few miles downhill, but men and beasts were too spent for another night in the open.

Six days later, only fifteen miles north of the Chitral-Darband junction, with the 24,000 foot peak of the Tirich Mir behind them, Zafar Ghazi and his exhausted caravan encountered the first Pakistani patrol, six soldiers led by a lieutenant.

'Where have you come from?' the lieutenant asked and Ghazi gave him a frank reply. 'From the Wakhjir in China.'

The lieutenant whistled. 'A long way . . .'

'Long, frosty and pestered by the Russians.'

'You were with Zebak Vahan?'

'Yes.'

'Then there must be a few less Russians on the far side of Baroghil.' The lieutenant seemed well informed, or knew Vahan.

'Eighty less, to be precise,' Mazar interrupted. 'And a number of pilots and officers.'

' "Masallah," ' the lieutenant complimented. 'Vahan is not afraid of anything . . .'

He walked round the covered sled, peered under the burlap and asked with a grin, 'Is this the shotgun you went to fetch from China?'

'Yes – we have a number of birds from the north in Nuristan to shoot at,' Mazar quipped. The lieutenant threw a level look at Ghazi and said quietly, 'You have to pay transit duty on imported foreign goods –'

'So Zebak told me,' Zafar handed the lieutenant a small bag of coins. 'That's fifty English guineas and Irani Rials in gold.' The lieutenant slipped the bag into his shoulder case.

'Very well, then, have a good trip home – and good hunting.'

After the Dorah Pass the snow fell less heavily and the gun was able to roll on its wheels, making the towing easier. But the sled was towed now, too, laden with ammunition boxes taken off the weary animals.

Zafar Ghazi was glad to have brought back all his men except two, laden with weapons and ammunition of inestimable value. The *mojahedins* of the Khawak Pass would be a proper army now, with modern weapons. Enemy convoys, even bases could be attacked from a distance. Roving copters and perhaps even MiGs could be shot down.

He moved on with the utmost care, to avoid being spotted by the Russians and Karmal's traitors. His task was not to fight, but to carry everything safely to the Khawak. As Zebak had done, he sent a dozen riders ahead to search for enemy blocking-parties. The easier route – through Sanglich and Kuran, then southward along the Karan stream to the Anjuman range and Khawak – was intercepted by a Russian regiment and Karmalists at Kuran. Zafar had to take the harder, but safer way across the Khama Pass to the village of Sinawi, then over the Ramgul to Khawak. None of the passes lay below 15,000 feet, and there was more ice and snow to tackle.

Mazar suggested sending some riders ahead, not only to survey the route, but to ride all the way home and advise Ali Ghazi of his brother's approach so that a relief team could come to meet them halfway. Zafar agreed, and decided to camp down at Sinawi where there would be food and shelter. As far as he knew, the little hamlet, 6,000 feet high up in the foothills of Ramgul, had not been visited by the invaders.

It was only 120 miles to Ghazi's camp as the crow flew, but overland the mileage lay closer to two hundred. Mazar, who was familiar with the route, reminded Ghazi of a fifteen-yard footbridge over a ravine in the Khama Pass that was neither wide nor strong enough for the gun to cross. They didn't have enough rope to ferry it across suspended, and he suggested he should ride ahead and organise some help. Zafar agreed, hoping too that his brother would come to meet them at the bridge. If they had to dismantle the gun completely, they'd need Dahi Baba, Gawar the engineer, and their mechanics.

Ahmad Mazar and another rider set out and Zafar Ghazi continued with the rest of his group, now only twenty-two strong and even more heavily laden. Half an hour advance, fifteen minutes rest became the order of the day. The horses and mules were at the end of their endurance and it took the caravan two days to cover twenty miles, struggling against head winds in knee-deep snow, shovelling corridors through twelve-foot drifts, spending freezing nights in the open. As might have been expected they did not meet a soul: the only imprints in the snow were those of Mazar and the others who had gone on ahead. Here and there the trail was strewn with fallen logs and boulders, swept down by recent storms and landslides, all of which had to be cleared. The *mojahedins* bore the hardship with remarkable patience and fortitude. No one complained. Every step brought them closer to the base and the well-deserved rest.

They reached the Khama Pass in five days and in knee-deep snow. Ahmad Mazar was already there camping in a makeshift tent made from a Russian parachute; with him were fifteen men from Sinawi, who had come on mules to help.

The flimsy footbridge over the two-hundred-foot ravine was only four hundred yards ahead. Zafar, Mazar and Parakin went to examine it and decided that it could only take the horses and mules, one by one. Slowly the caravan moved across, while Mazar and the villagers began the work of building a ferry for the gun, using the ropes, tools and eight strong hooks they had brought along. In five hours the ferry was ready: the sled with the gun hung suspended and a team of six horses hauled it over the ravine.

In Sinawi, they spent their first night indoors after thirteen days, and the impoverished villagers treated them with the best they had. Two days later Ali Ghazi rode in with forty men and the days of hardship were over.

Their reception at Dahi Baba's caves was tumultuous. The guerrillas cheered them and exulted over the sleek rapid-fire gun, the bazookas and mortars. The automatic rifles Ali Ghazi distributed on the spot, with a generous number of cartridges and hand-grenades. The pair of machine guns which Zebak had presented to Zafar went to protect the trail between the Khawak and the caves.

Ali suggested that the gun should be used only along the passable trail between the Khawak, Dasht-i-Rewat, Banu and Zardaspan, where a pair of horses could easily move it. The plan was never to leave it in the same position for longer than a day, but roll it between specially prepared shelters. Since the mountains were already under snow, Dahi Baba painted it white, and the mortars as well. Thirty snowsuits from Zebak Vahan were also distributed, and Ali Ghazi organised his first properly equipped assault group of forty *mojahedins* – the core of a real 'army', as he said, and he was very contented.

Zafar Ghazi stuck to his rapid-fire gun and earnestly wished that some copters would show up around the Khawak Pass. They stayed away during most of the winter, but squadrons of MiG fighters frequently flew over the Pass. Zafar could have fired at them, but wisely refrained: he had no wish to give away the presence of the AA gun before the copters arrived by shooting the sky full of holes. He needed some real experience before trying to tackle the fast-flying fighters.

But he did his best to learn, without wasting ammunition. Whenever the weather permitted he went to exercise, 'firing dry' at distant targets, cliffs, trees, and boulders, shifting aim rapidly, following high-flying vultures with the twin-barrels, until he had got the feeling of speed and distances and could execute rapid shifts with considerable skill.

THE TERRIBLE OATH OF ABI SAFED

JIM HAD gone to Pakistan with his haul of local antiques – a good three mule-loads of old guns, rugs, knives, household utensils and even an ancient Singer sewing machine – which the *mojahedins* had collected for him over the months. They even made a slight detour, so that Jim could go through Customs and have his booty properly declared at the frontier. Then he'd have no difficulty when trying to export them from Pakistan.

Bazi Noor, Ali Jamrad and a quiet, unsmiling guerrilla by the name of Abi Safed accompanied him. Apart from transporting Jim's goods, the men had been given a long list of useful hardware to buy for the base in the Khawak. It was late November and already freezing cold when they returned to Ghazi's camp, clad in furs and cursing the weather, the cold, the snow and the Russian patrol which had given them a spirited chase and killed one of the mules.

They brought back a small Japanese generator for Dahi Baba, four crates of dynamite, ten large coils of fuse wire – about a hundred yards altogether – and six hundred percussion caps, not to mention a quantity of nails, nuts and bolts, tools and tobacco. Needless to say, everyone was delighted. Jim had even thought to bring a small box of precious medicines: antibiotics, painkillers, some surgical knives and scissors, wound-clamps, chloroform, ether, antiseptic pads and sterile bandages. The Khawak had no doctors or nurses, but he thought his basic first-aid training in the army would at least ease the suffering of the wounded guerrillas and even perhaps save lives.

Ali Ghazi beamed like a torchlight and Mazar crushed the Englishman in his customary bearhug, booming: 'Jim, you are the best accursed infidel in the world – you're already a half brother . . . You should embrace Islam. Afghanistan is a fine country and will soon be free again. We could give you a bit of land, build you a good house – even get you three pretty wives.'

The *mojahedins* rocked with laughter, while Jim declined the offer with a grin.

'It's extremely kind of you, Ahmad, but I don't know a damn thing about farming and I've already got a wife.'

'Mohammed allows you to have three,' Mazar retorted chuckling.

'Unfortunately my wife is not so liberal. Her maiden name is Fury – if you know what the word stands for.'

'Angry,' engineer Gawar cut in.

'More than angry – raving,' said Jim and Mazar chuckled again.

'Where is she, in Pakistan?'

'In England, thank God – but she wants me back there as fast as possible.'

'You ought to bring her here instead, Jim. Women have little say in Afghanistan.'

'Your Mohammed was a very wise man. Three wives in the household and not one of them allowed to open her mouth . . . A good arrangement.'

'Woman talk a lot of nonsense, anyway,' said Mazar, and his companions murmured their cheerful agreement.

Engineer Gawar showed Dahi Baba how the generator worked and the little old man with his white beard and bow legs bounced round it like a happy elf. He had every reason to rejoice: now he could run his machine tools on power and use an arc-welder. The dynamite would be used to make land mines against tanks and troop carriers. Tin cans filled with rusty nails, fragments of metal and glass and a stick of dynamite could kill plenty of enemy infantry. And Musa Gawar had other ingenious designs as well such as sticks of dynamite fitted to arrows and launched from strongbows to fly much further than a man could throw them. He had made a few dry runs and worked out that the arrow-borne explosive could easily go a hundred yards, even with a light cowling to protect the burning fuse and prevent the missile from being spotted at night. Experimenting with fuses, he soon determined the proper lengths for three types of projectiles, designed to explode more or less on impact at thirty, seventy and a hundred yards.

Dahi Baba asked Jim warily.

'Was the money we gave you enough to buy everything you brought back?'

'Enough, my foot,' said Jim, pulling his leg. 'I contributed two hundred and forty pounds of my own. To get the dynamite and the fuse we rode all the way to the Mianwali coal mines . . . The director, a German engineer – a most reasonable chap – said he couldn't sell or give away company property, but if we waited a couple of days, he would go to Lahore and leave his foreman, Hassan Mujibullah in charge. So we waited. Mujibullah was a very reasonable fellow, too, most sympathetic to the Afghan cause, especially when he saw a bundle of pound notes. He said there could always be a few more sticks recorded on the daily reports than had actually been used. He did lots of extra blastings in the mine to save up four crates for you.'

He wrinkled his nose and added with a wink; 'So, Baba – you owe me two hundred pounds for the generator and forty for the dynamite.'

Taking him at face value the old man said, 'Give us a few days and we'll pay you back, Jim.'

'In sterling?' asked Jim.

'In gold,' Ali Ghazi cut in. Seeing that he really meant it, Jim patted him on the shoulder. 'Don't worry about it, Ali. It looks as if I'll be around for a while – the roads are all snowed up and it's hard to run away from the Russian snow-mobiles.'

'What's that?' Mazar glanced up, startled, and engineer Gawar explained what a snowmobile was to the group of astonished listeners.

'Do the Russians have many such vehicles, Jim?' Ghazi asked grimly.

'Well, I presume the Red Army wouldn't import just the one that came after us near Daolatshah . . . ' It only carried three Russians and a mounted heavy machine gun, but it came charging up the slope at thirty miles an hour, firing all the time.' He paused for a moment to sip his tea. 'I must say it was a pretty close shave – I began to wonder whether I'd be shot, hanged, or asked to make amends in some gulag in Siberia . . . Fortunately there was a ravine between us, which gave the Russians a bit of trouble, but I think they would have managed to cross it.'

'Why didn't they?' Ali Ghazi asked. 'What happened?'

'The snowmobile ran out of petrol,' Jim said with a grin, but Ali missed the point. The enemy would never go anywhere without enough fuel. 'Ask Noor, he was responsible.'

Smiling modestly, Bazi Noor recounted how he and Abi Safed had fallen behind to delay the pursuit, so that Jim and the others could reach the safety of the woods with the pack mules.

'I tossed two sticks of dynamite into the ravine . . . Not very effective in deep snow, but they still damaged the fuel tank – the snowmobile stopped, with petrol spilling all over the place. Two of the Russians died, but the third one kept firing until the car began to burn and set fire to his padded jacket.'

Jim cut in: 'He was still rolling in the snow when Abi Safed shot him between the eyes.' He bit his lip. 'He just stood over the fellow, staring at him, and took aim. The Russki screamed, and Abi told him to shut up and shot him between the eyes . . . He's a cool customer that Abi Safed. In all the weeks we spent together he spoke about fifteen words and I haven't seen him smile once.'

'When a man loses his wife and three children to the Russians, Jim,' Ali Ghazi Khan said quietly, 'he loses his smiles, as well.'

'Oh, no . . . No one told me . . . '

'You never asked. The Afghans are not talkative people.'

'Poor Abi . . . '

'Safed has killed thirty-two Russians with his own hands and many more with his gun. I think he only keeps going in order to kill Russians.' Ali Ghazi paused to light his pipe, offered Jim a light and went on, puffing: 'I'll tell you his story one day – only to show why the enemy can never beat us into submission.'

'Do,' said Jim. 'I'm truly curious.'

The enemy's introduction of snowmobiles worried Ali Ghazi and he questioned Jim and engineer Gawar about them in detail. The fact that the agile vehicles were able to do forty miles an hour on snowy lands visibly disturbed him. 'It is very important that you told me all this,' he told Jim. 'The enemy might embark on a winter campaign just when we consider the trails impassable.'

'You have the trails well protected anyway . . . '

'But the Russians might land those vehicles by helicopters.'

Jim shrugged. 'That's why you got the Chinese gun.'

Ali Ghazi shook his head. 'It's not easy to move that gun in deep snow. When the horses sink chest deep, they can't haul a thing.'

'Well, then – we'd better start thinking how to knock out some of their snowmobiles,' Jim said calmly, as if it were the most natural proposal to make. The *mojahedins* of the Khawak were by now well used to Jim's off-the-cuff solutions. Ever since his successful bazooka attack against the helicopter gunship, everything he suggested was seriously considered.

The dynamite-tipped arrows were tested. A man of average strength could easily hurl the explosive a hundred yards; the bulging muscles of Ahmad Mazar sent them much further.

'I think I rather like this Robin Hood life,' Jim remarked after he had blasted a pile of rocks at eighty yards. Then he reminded Ali Ghazi that flying fragments of dynamite could also do well against low-flying, or hovering copters.

Another specialist group was born. As well as the Kalachnikovs and the light, Polish WZ machine pistols, its members were also equipped with dynamite-tipped arrows. Each *mojahedin* was now virtually a one-man artillery.

'What do you think of them?' Ali Ghazi Khan asked Jim with obvious pride.

'They look like a pack of Tartars of a space-age Batu Khan, but I think when they go into action, the Russians won't feel too happy.'

Later that evening, Ali Ghazi told Jim the story of Abi Safed.

*   *   *

98

At twenty-eight, Abi Safed was a hard-working, peaceful peasant, who owned just enough land to support his family and a small flock of sheep. He knew little of the outside world – which as far as he was concerned ended a few miles beyond his village, Miagan – until the terrible day he lost his family in a Russian air raid. The MiG's came to 'retaliate' for a dozen shotgun pellets a feeble-minded old shepherd had fired against a copter which wanted to land some surveyors engaged in the Jalalabad irrigation project. No one was hurt in the silly incident except the shepherd, whom the pilot dispatched with a short machine pistol salvo. But soon afterwards the six MiGs came 'to eliminate a dangerous rebel nest' in Miagan. The fighter-bombers machine-gunned, bombed and rocketed the village into heaps of smouldering debris, an act no doubt recorded as one of great heroism.

Gathering stones for a wall half a mile away Abi Safed saw his house going up in smoke and flame.

Eighty dead and one hundred and eleven wounded. Almost the entire population had perished, or would be invalids for ever: Abi Safed found himself alone and homeless.

He buried his loved ones, washed his hands, took the Holy Koran and made a solemn but terrible oath: no day would go past until he had killed a Russian – for every year his wife and three children had lived. He would not sleep at night until his daily oath had been fulfilled.

His wife, Aynar, was only twenty-two: his children were five, three and two years old.

Thirty-two Russian lives for Abi Safed's family.

He sold his sheep, his pair of horses and the cart, and three donkeys, keeping only one mule for himself. He tucked away the money in his turban and waistcloth, knowing that he would have no time to look for work. He already had a job. Killing Russians.

He did not join any of the *mojahedin* groups active in the region: the movements of the guerrillas were restricted and whole days could go by without their killing a single Russian. Abi Safed had to kill one that day if he wanted to sleep that night.

As well as the money, he tucked away the old dagger he

had inherited from his father. Ten inches long and honed razor sharp, it was a weapon well-suited for his purpose. He would have preferred to carry a shotgun, or a pistol, but controls were frequent in the towns and on the roads leading to them – and besides, firearms made a lot of noise. The places where he might find his daily victims would be crowded with people. The death he wanted to deal should be swift and silent.

He also took a small tin can and a canvas bag for collecting other silent killers, such as snakes and scorpions: he knew where to find them.

Abi Safed rode to Besud and crossed the Kabul river to Jalalabad. The place was crowded with invaders, many of them civilians; it made no difference to him, as long as they were Russians.

His first victim was an engineer, working on the dykes. It was easy for Abi Safed to pass himself off as one of the workmen, just long enough to get behind the Russian and slit his throat.

Then he rode off a few miles and went to sleep in the riverside shrubs.

Thirty-one . . .

The next day he considered a lucky one. He spotted a small group of soldiers strolling about the bazaar. He tailed them for over an hour until he found one who had wandered away from the group and was surrounded by a crowd of peddlers. Abi plunged the dagger into the soldier's back all the way to the heart, withdrew it and melted into the crowd before his victim collapsed.

Thirty . . .

He was already out in the street and walking away leading his mule, when Karmal's police and Russian troops sealed the bazaar to frisk a thousand people, looking for the assassin.

The following day was wasted, for although he did find a few invaders, circumstances prevented him from killing any of them without endangering himself. He could not risk capture, or death, at least not before he had fulfilled his oath. That night, sleepless, he rode his mule to Kabul, pondering bitterly over the mistake he had made: he should have made a different oath: to kill thirty-two Russians was enough without specifying time.

But Allah is Great, and guards the faithful!

A few miles before Gandamaz, he came across a Soviet lorry, one of many which twice a week transported vegetables and cereals to the garrison in Kabul. It had been attacked by the *mojahedins* and lay on its side in the ditch with its load spilling into the road. The driver and two soldiers had been shot, but another lorry, an armoured troop carrier with twelve soldiers and an Afghani sergeant, had drawn up alongside. The soldiers were busy transferring sacks of potatoes, beans and maize, sweating and swearing incessantly. Abi Safed halted, greeted the sergeant with a quiet *'Salem aleikum'* and asked if he could help. His offer was accepted readily enough. Safed walked his mule thirty paces from the road and tethered it to a bush, then began to haul sacks from the ditch, carrying them to the lorry on the road. Neither the Russians nor the sergeant paid any attention to him: the lean-faced, undernourished peasant was surely not a rebel. Abi Safed waited for his chance.

At long last a shaven-headed, snub-nosed corporal strolled into the bushes to relieve himself. Safed glanced towards the road, then walked after the Russian, and caught him with his pants down. Clamping one hand over his mouth, he stabbed him in the heart, twisting the dagger. Blood spurted on to his hand; in moments the Russian was dead. It was still dark enough. Abi Safed untied his mule and trotted away northwards into the hills towards the river, where he lay down in a an empty shepherd's hut and went to sleep.

Allah was with him.

Twenty-nine . . .

Abi Safed's next victim was the sergeant driver of a Russian colonel, who sat at the wheel of a parked army car while the colonel's wife read a magazine in the back seat. The open bazaar crawled with people: a noisy, milling crowd of men, carts, mules and camels. Peddlers called out their wares, beggars cried for alms, carts clattered and horns blared impatiently.

It was July, the air stagnant and oppressively hot. The

windows of the car were open a few inches: wide enough for Abi Safed to slip through a yellow-banded viper, right into the sergeant's lap.

He melted into the crowd.

The woman screamed and sprang from the car, followed by the sergeant, tearing the reptile from his bleeding wrist. The crowd surged towards them, then drew back, terrified, and canes swished through the air, striking the snake. From a safe distance, Abi Safed watched the scene.

The colonel came running and comforted his hysterical wife. The sergeant tore off his uniform jacket, and someone applied a tourniquet to his elbow. Calmly, Abi Safed strolled back and joined the chattering crowd. His face ashen, beads of perspiration glittering on his forehead, the sergeant was muttering garbled words. An elderly man with betel-stained gums leaned over the wound to suck out the venom. 'Don't do it,' Safed warned him in a quiet, terse voice. 'If you have a bad tooth, or a cut in your mouth, you will die, too . . . ' The helper frowned and rose hesitantly.

A police car arrived, and the crowd parted. The sergeant was helped to the rear seat with the colonel and his terrified wife and the police car roared off, its siren screaming. Two officers remained on the scene to guard the colonel's vehicle and question the bystanders.

No one had seen the culprit.

Abi Safed felt content. He would sleep tonight. The hospital was miles away, the streets jammed with carts and mules and the yellow-banded viper was a swift killer.

Twenty-eight . . .

Abi Safed continued to fulfil his oath, spreading terror wherever he went, and he moved between the Russian-infested localities a great deal. The Russians wanted him. Karmal's police offered a handsome reward for information on the 'madman'. Abi Safed could not read, but he bought a newspaper and went to sit in an open-air barber's chair to have his beard trimmed. He asked the barber casually if there was anything in the paper about the 'madman' who was killing Russians. The barber scanned the pages and shook his head. 'Not a word,' he told Safed, then added; 'And there never will be – Karmal would never admit that anyone in Afghanistan would kill our dear Russian friends and benefactors.'

Abi Safed moved on. In Kabul he struck down four Russians: three in the bazaars of Shahre Nan and Seraye Ghazni; one in Kote-e-Singi, in the outhouse of a roadside tavern, where travellers stopped for a *shashlik*, a cut of roast lamb, and tea or coffee.

There were nights when his oath forbade him to sleep, but Allah would never let him down. He always guided some stray invaders into Abi Safed's path.

He went to Charikar, avoiding the closely patrolled main road, and took the trail through Ak Sarai and Karabagh in the northern foothills of the Koh-i-Baba range.

By the grace of Allah the High and Benevolent, he bumped into a Russian helicopter landed on a clearing with an engine defect. The two pilots were visibly terrified, for they did not know where they were and kept Abi Safed covered with their machine pistols while they questioned him about directions and asked if there were any rebels in the neighbourhood. Safed spoke no Russian, but he understood the words 'Charikar', 'Kabul' and *mojahedin*, and he understood their gestures. He wondered why the pilots would not radio for help, until one of them explained, 'Niet radio – radio kaputt.'

With the friendliest of words and gestures, Safed reassured the Russians that he was not a *mojahedin* – there were no *mojahedins* in the neighbourhood. He showed them that he carried no weapon and even offered the men a hunk of roast lamb. He kept bread and salt in his bag. The one offered bread and salt would not be killed.

In the end he was accepted as a peaceful peasant from the village across the hills, and when he offered to guide one of the Russians to Ak Sarai, where mules could be hired for the twenty-two mile ride to Charikar, the pilots accepted.

Like a good host he lent his mule to the Russian and led it along the winding trail until they came to a spring. There Safed stopped to drink and fill his small waterbag. The Russian dismounted and came over to drink himself. Abi

103

Safed waited until he had bent down and stabbed him three times in the back.

He tucked the infidel's pistol into his 'shash' and shouldered the machine pistol – not that he wanted to keep them: firearms would be dangerous to carry around – but he might meet some *mojahedins* who could surely use the weapons.

He dragged the corpse into the underbrush, then camped down at the spring for the rest of the day, and a good night's sleep. His victim for tomorrow was comfortably close and he was in no hurry to go anywhere.

Twenty-three . . .

Abi Safed rose early and rode back to the copter. The other pilot was asleep in his locked cockpit. Abi Safed settled down in the nearby bushes and waited patiently until he woke up and came into the open to piss.

He shot him in the head, collected his weapon too, then set fire to the copter.

Allah is great!

Twenty-two . . .

He rode off towards Ak Sarai and Charikar and half an hour later bumped into a group of twelve *mojahedins* led by his namesake, Safed Yar, who had come to investigate the smoke and fire. Abi Safed gave them the weapons and having learned about his oath and what he had done, Safed Yar embraced him and kissed him on both cheeks and the *mojahedins* followed his example. 'We have three Russian prisoners in our camp,' Yar told Abi Safed, inviting him into his village. 'I'll give them to you, so that you can have three nights' sleep.'

Abi Safed went off with the *mojahedins* and had his sleep.

Eighteen . . .

The oath given upon the Holy Koran had to be fulfilled. Had he sworn to cut off his left hand if he failed, he would have cut if off without hesitation.

His solemn oath was brought to fulfilment in Charikar and along the highway to Doshi and the USSR, with the help of Safed Yar and his guerrillas, who went to hunt for Russians and brought them back to Abi Safed unhurt, or wounded, to be executed by him.

When the thirty-second invader had died, Abi Safed washed his face, his feet and hands, rinsed his mouth and went to pray in the mosque.

' "La illaha il Allah, hak Mohammed abdu ve arrasu-lullah." '

But strangely the fulfilment of his terrible oath did not quench his thirst for Russian blood. After thirty-two kililings, Abi Safed had become addicted to watching his enemy die. It made him feel good, when he saw them spilling blood and kicking their last; doubly so when, frisking his victims, he found family photos of wives and children.

An eye for an eye . . .

Allah is great. Allah had permitted him to fulfil his oath and remain unscathed. Perhaps he had a mission.

Abi Safed set out on the long trek to the Khawak to join the *mojahedins* of Ali Ghazi Khan, already famous in the district, and it was not long before the number of his victims had doubled. But even then he preferred his knife, a noose, or bare hands to any firearm. And when one evening Jim casually asked him how he could ever do it, Abi Safed said in a quiet, indifferent voice: 'To kill from a distance calls for no sentiments and gives me no satisfaction. The infidel enemy should *know* that he is about to die. I must feel the flesh of my enemy, see the terror in his eyes, the veins in his neck pumping wildly, hear his last gasp . . . I want to see in his face that he repents the very day when he set foot in our country. Besides,' he added after a brief pause, 'the way I fight them, I have more of a chance to survive. None of my enemies have ever had a chance to fight back . . . Many of my companions think that I am a very brave man, but it is not true, Jim. When I kill, it does not call for bravery. I only think of my wife, my children . . . Not even of my country. If I could, I would go to Moscow and kill Russians on the streets . . . kill thousands of them. It would make no difference to me.'

'Will you be ever able to stop killing, Abi?'

'I am not a madman,' came the quiet answer. 'When there are no more infidel invaders in Afghanistan, I will go home and rebuild my house. But not before.

KARMAL'S RELUCTANT ARMY

THE ANTICIPATED snowmobile attack never materialised. The enemy ground forces stayed away from the mountains, but whenever the weather permitted the Russian Air Force continued its work of destruction. The MiGs were active around the Khawak Pass, but still bombed and strafed the wrong sites, causing no damage to the *mojahedins*. Zafar Ghazi shot down another copter and damaged three MiGs, one of which was seen losing altitude between two peaks, leaving a trail of smoke.

The guerrillas embarked on a series of quick raids against Russian and Karmalist installations and their arrow-borne dynamite proved quite deadly. The projectiles travelled in perfect silence, struck from the dead of night, and there were no muzzle-flashes to enable the enemy gunners to orient themselves.

Road blocks, stationary army vehicles, Karmalist police stations, army checkpoints, radar and telephone installations, fuel tankers and supply convoys – all fell victim to Ali Ghazi's arrow-borne 'artillery'. Unlike rifles and other firearms, unstrung bows and arrows were easy to smuggle past police and army checkpoints and into the cities, mostly hidden in carts laden with firewood. The frequently used metal detectors did not pick them up there. After use, or whenever it was necessary, the bows were destroyed. New ones could be made in two hours. Sitting in high windows, in closed yards, perching on trees, rooftops and minarets, Ghazi's bowmen would blow up a platoon of marching troops, a loaded truck, or official vehicles driving along the nearby road, without any danger of being spotted and arrested.

During the winter months the *mojahedins* carried the war into the towns and killed a large number of Russians, including a group of engineers and technicians, who burned to death in a blown-up barracks at Jalalabad. Ahmad Mazar blew up a Soviet general's limousine, but could not ascertain if the general had actually been travelling in it. The Karmalist news media would never even mention successful guerrilla actions.

'I wish I could sit on top of the Pamir building,' Mazar grumbled. The Pamir was the tallest structure in Kabul. 'You could send an arrow five hundred yards from up there.'

Bazi Noor hit a petrol tanker which set alight the entrance of a Soviet housing complex. Fuel tankers were the favourite targets of Ghazi's dynamite snipers: a single hit could cause immense damage and the ensuing confusion would always ensure the sniper's safe escape.

Among other important targets hit and severely damaged was a restaurant on Kabul's Yadeh-Ye-Maiwand street, much frequented by Russians and a regional office of the Communist 'Parcham' party, where forty people attending a meeting were killed, or severely wounded.

One of Abi Safed's long shots caught a busload of East German civilians, who had just landed in Kabul on some unknown but probably sinister mission, and were being transported to the Mikrorayon Soviet housing centre. Eight of them died, six were taken into the hospital of the Soviet base. And what Abi Safed enjoyed most about that particular escapade was that after the terrific blast he could join the helpers to 'rescue' the East Germans trapped in the twisted wreckage. The street was in uproar with people running all over the place, shouting for help, and asking what had happened. Afghan soldiers and passers-by endeavoured to free the trapped foreigners and Abi Safed joined them 'to lend a hand'. No one saw him choke the last spark of life from a moaning man, while 'trying to bind his wounded neck'. Looking for someone else to 'rescue' he spotted a short, plump man with a briefcase chained to his left wrist. He sat slumped between a pair of twisted seats with a sliver of window-frame sticking out of his stomach like the hilt of a dagger. Lifting him gently, Safed pushed the fragment deeper and twisted it round. His victim stopped breathing and Abi

Safed carried him outside. He laid the corpse next to the others, telling the white-faced Karmalist lieutenant. 'This one is dead too.' And he called the officer's attention to the brief-case, 'which might contain something important'. He was thanked for his attention and given ten packs of cigarettes. At last the ambulances arrived from the Soviet base. Abi Safed strolled back into the roadside garden of a baker friend, picked up his bow and hurled the remaining two sticks of dynamite into the group of ambulances.

He tossed the bow into the baker's furnace, mounted his mule and trotted off towards Perwan with a sack of bread, as innocent as a new-born baby. At the army roadblock even his loaves were tested with metal detectors.

Safed enjoyed this silent kind of warfare as much as the enemy hated it. A week later he learned that his last couple of shots had wrecked four ambulances with six wounded infidels already inside them; three Russian doctors, five nurses, an Afghan officer and several Karmalists had also fallen victim to the double blast.

Ahmad Mazar tried to persuade Jim to come along on one of these hunting trips, but he laughingly declined the invitation, reminding Mazar that he was in the country without a visa – or a passport, for that matter. Besides, he preferred hunting for foxes in the Khawak, to take a furcoat home to his wife.

'When they catch you, Ahmad, you'll probably hang on the tallest lampost in Kabul,' he said. 'If they catch me,' I'd probably hang on *every* lampost from Kabul to Herat, the bloody American spy I am.'

'But you're not an American,' Mazar guffawed.

'I don't think a British spy would be good enough for the Kremlin,' Jim said. 'They'd want one from the CIA . . . But once in their hands, I would probably confess to being one of the assistant directors. One never disappoints the Soviet GRU . . . You know, I heard a good story about a Russian archeological expedition which found a skeleton rigged out in gold, somewhere in Mongolia. They couldn't agree whose remains it might have been, so they sent it to the secret police in Moscow for identification. A few weeks later the museum received a bagful of broken bones and the skull with all its teeth knocked out, and a note saying: "The suspect has confessed to having been known as Kublai Khan, and has signed the enclosed statement." '

The *mojahedins* fell about laughing. Then Safak Parakin came up with a story of his own. 'Someone is hammering on the door of farmer Ivan Ivanovich at the dead of night. Scared stiff, he tiptoes to the door and moans, "Who is it?" A deep voice booms from outside: "I am the devil, and you must come with me to hell." Ivanovich heaves a happy sigh of relief and says: "Thank God, I thought it was the police."

The rest of the evening was spent swapping jokes and stories about the Russians, Babrak Karmal and his traitors. It was important to keep their spirits up in the silent loneliness of the snow.

Throughout the winter the helicopters rarely showed themselves and the Russian infantry remained in their barracks near Charikar. Kabul dispatched two companies of Afghan troops under the command of a captain. Supervised by two Russian observers of equal rank, he was to test the rebel positions near the Khawak Pass and plan for an eventual attack later on.

The Karmalists came by armed troop carriers to Dasht-i-Rewat, then continued on foot to look for the mysterious rebel base and – as Ali Ghazi pointed out – for trouble.

His brother Zafar and Ahmad Mazar were resolved to fight and give the traitors of Karmal a lasting lesson, but Ali Ghazi had a different idea. He deployed two hundred of his fighters on either side of the valley's narrow, winding road, but told them not to fire until he gave the signal, and even then to fire only as a warning, not to kill. Since the Karmalists were obviously looking for him, he decided to meet them halfway, face to face, and alone. He had a plan.

The chosen guerrillas covered the approach with machine guns and dynamite. The Chinese AA-gun was set up close to the bend where Ali wanted to meet the oncoming columns of soldiers.

Two hundred yards ahead of the first company marched an advance guard of four young soldiers, probably new conscripts and obviously scared, for they kept looking from left to right, constantly surveying the rugged slopes as if expecting to be shot at any moment. The captain and the lieutenant at his side carried submachine guns; likewise the Russian observers, apparently trying their best to keep themselves covered by the Afghan soldiers.

Leaving his weapons behind, Ali Ghazi mounted a mule and trotted down the road towards the troops. His companions watched him uneasily. They had a good view of Ali and the oncoming detachment half a mile below, but only two sharp bends separated Ghazi from the advance guard. Presently he came into sight and the soldiers stopped and stared at the lone rider coming towards them. Passing by, Ali Ghazi greeted them with a quiet 'Salem aleikum' and rode on, untroubled by the baffled looks which followed him. The soldiers stared after him for a few moments, then shrugged and resumed their wary advance.

When Ali trotted into view the captain raised his hand and the column halted. Ten paces from the officers, Ali Ghazi halted too, and alighted from his mule. He greeted the captain and his companions civilly and asked where the soldiers were heading.

'These are very hostile mountains and Ali Ghazi Khan does not like uninvited visitors,' he said mildly.

The officers were startled by the nonchalantly delivered warning. The two Russians stepped closer and inquired what Ali had said and the lieutenant translated the gist of it. 'Have you seen any guerrillas further uphill?' the captain asked and Ghazi rocked his head from side to side in the Oriental expression of the affirmative. 'I wouldn't go any further if I were you,' he said quietly, lighting his pipe. 'It was unwise enough for you to leave Dasht-i-Rewat . . . The Khawak belongs to the *mojahedins*, Captain.'

'Skolko partizanski?' one of the Russians cut in. 'How many guerrillas are there?'

'In the Anjuman range every cliff, every tree and every ravine is a guerrilla,' Ali replied enigmatically.

'Who are you?' the lieutenant asked.

Ghazi shifted his face towards him. 'I am the man you've come to see – Ali Ghazi.'

'Ali Ghazi Khan?' the lieutenant blurted, staring at him incredulously.

'The very man . . . '

His casual announcement had the effect of a suddenly exploded bomb. Ignoring the officers' baffled faces, Ghazi turned round and raised his hand. A short salvo of machine guns and automatic rifles thundered into the uneasy silence to echo and re-echo between the cliffs. Smiling, Ghazi turned towards the far side of the ravine and raised his other hand. The response came in the shape of four dynamite-tipped arrows, blasting the boulder-strewn slope. The troops broke ranks, and began to talk wildly, casting terrified glances in every direction, trying to spot the invisible enemy. Then Zafar's AA-gun opened up, firing into the ravine, blasting boulders, mud and snow. And the Afghan officers realised they were trapped.

Pointing out a towering boulder which overhung the road four hundred yards downhill, Ghazi said, 'That cliff over there is mined and we can blast it over the road at any moment.' He flung a leg over the mule's back and mounted, adding casually, 'You could kill me, of course, but it would make no difference. You would all die a few minutes later, Captain.' He glanced at the two Russians who stared at him, pale and stricken, and added nonchalantly; 'you could also kill the two Russians and join us, or you could hand over your weapons and return to Dasht-i-Rewat in peace . . . You have ten minutes to decide.'

He nudged his mule to turn, and the lieutenant called after him tersely. 'Why kill them? They can't do any harm.'

'They've already done enough harm, Lieutenant,' Ali replied. 'You should come and see the villages around Banu . . . We are always ready to spare our brother Afghans, but we don't have the same feelings about the invaders.'

He noted with satisfaction that his offer was already being considered. 'Ten minutes,' he repeated and began trotting uphill. He did not expect to be shot in the back, and smiled at the heated dispute which broke out behind him, and among the ranks: an angry altercation mixed with harsh Russian shouts and swearing. He came to the advance party, now resting on a boulder with their guns between their knees, smoking. They rose and one of them said timidly to Ali: 'My companions and I – we would like to join you, Ghazi Khan.'

Ghazi slapped him on the shoulders and beckoned to the others.

'What are you waiting for?' And he moved on. The soldiers shouldered their rifles and marched after him, obviously very happy about the turn of events. The troops down the road cheered, and reversed their arms, signalling that they had no intention of firing at the *mojahedins*.

A sergeant stepped forward, drew his automatic and coolly emptied the magazine into the Russian officers, while the captain and the lieutenant looked on bewildered. The sergeant kicked the two corpses into the ravine and called after Ali Ghazi: 'I am with you, Ghazi Khan!'

Ghazi halted to wait for the Karmalist column.

'You have won, Ghazi Khan,' said the captain with a faint smile. He put out his hand and Ali took it. 'My name is Sadek Karatash. My companion – Lieutenant Yamrad Karam.'

Ali said afterwards; 'You are mistaken. It is not Ghazi who won, but the Afghan people.'

Two hundred and twenty soldiers decided to join him.

Ghazi turned to Captain Karatash. 'What about you two, Captain?'

The captain opened his hands. 'We have our families in Charikar. What will happen to them?'

'We can bring them into the Khawak.'

'How?'

'Let's discuss it later, in the camp.'

The two officers had not only changed sides, but promptly prepared a plan for a raid against the Soviet base at Charikar. The first step was to seize the armoured troop carriers left in Dasht-i-Rewat: they could easily pass the road blocks and reach the enemy base without arousing suspicion.

Then came the devastating news: Acar Yarim, a one-time

robber turned patriot, whose men were active around the Baigakh Pass in the Hindukush, had swept down on the troop carriers the same day, killed or beaten off the detachment of guards and drivers and set fire to the vehicles.

Yarim's raid ruined Ali Ghazi's plan. It also caused many casualties and did a great deal of damage in the village. The soldiers left behind to guard the troop carriers were still unaware that their officers and comrades had deserted, and finding themselves surrounded, the sergeant in charge radioed for help. The Soviet Command at Jalalabad dispatched a squadron of MiGs which bombed and rocketed the village for twenty minutes, covering the withdrawal along the road to Perwan of three vehicles still serviceable. Acar Yarim lost half of his group, retired into the Hindukush and claimed a great victory. More jets and copters came to play merry-go-round over the Anjuman, trying to find the missing Afghan detachment, looking for signs of ground battle and firing into the wilderness at random.

Captain Karatash and Lieutenant Karam were mortified at the loss of the armoured carriers. Ali Ghazi Khan raged and Mazar cursed Acar Yarim, his *mojahedins* and the rivalry between guerrilla groups in the region.

'Yarim is a good patriot, but a damned hothead and one day he will die in some stupid accident,' Mazar grumbled and his companions murmured agreement. All of them had heard of Yarim's ill-begotten attempt to blow up the northern entrance of the all-important Salang tunnel on the highway between the Soviet base at Mazar-i-Sharif and Kabul, ignoring the warnings of his older companions. The 9500-foot tunnel along the only supply route to and from the USSR was very heavily guarded. Nonetheless, Acar Yarim set out with seventy men, fifty pounds of explosive and plenty of patriotic fervour. After several days marching over difficult terrain and dodging copter and fighter patrols, Acar's group arrived within half a mile of the tunnel only to run into a patch of densely packed RG-42 'jump mines' which, when touched off, sprang five feet into the air and exploded in the victim's face. The sound raised the enemy defences: search-lights illuminated the whole area and the neighbouring machine gun positions opened up on the fleeing guerrillas. Yarim lost all his pack mules and thirty-five fighters in the abortive attempt.

Despite such grave losses he would not give up. Enraged by his failure, the following night he doubled back to the road, and using the rest of the explosives managed to blow up two Russian trucks carrying winter clothes, and a Quadri Company bus occupied by more civilians than Karmalist soldiers returning to Kabul from leave.

'Unless you coordinate your actions in future, you won't make any headway against the Soviets at all,' Jim commented on the incident at Dasht-i-Rewat and Ali Ghazi agreed with him. He estimated that there were at least fifteen independent groups of *mojahedins* operating in the Parwan-Daolatshah-Zardaspan-Doshi quadrangle which embraced some 3,200 square miles of mountain country.

The next morning the sun shone. The clear sky over the Khawak Pass was alive with screaming jets and clattering copters searching for the 'lost' companies of Captain Karatash. Ali Ghazi decided not to open fire. His brother Zafar felt frustrated at the sight of so many copters buzzing within easy range, but he admitted that Ali was right. Enemy air presence was too strong and the downing of a few copters would have initiated a massive bombardment and perhaps caused the loss of the AA-gun.

The defectors brought six walkie-talkies and a powerful transmitter to the Khawak. 'We're getting modernised,' engineer Musa Gawar remarked cheerfully, dreaming of future actions, well-timed and coordinated, involving several groups of *mojahedins* moving miles apart. The large short-wave transmitter-receiver, with its range of several hundred miles, would one day make possible coordinated actions across the whole of Afghanistan. Ali Ghazi decided that until another similar set could be sequestered from somewhere, Safak Parakin should use the single unit for eavesdropping on Red Army communications. He could then transmit regular daily bulletins to the Russian troops, telling the truth about the situation in Afghanistan, which their political officers were eager to cover up.

114

It was also decided to assign the two Afghan Army officers and their troops to the Anjuman Pass, fifteen miles north of the Khawak, where another spacious cave, with long passages, provided convenient cover.

A couple of days later, Zafar Ghazi downed another helicopter gunship which crash-landed in the riverbed but did not burn. Its crew of five tried to flee and were shot. The copter yielded another large wireless set, a pair of heavy machine guns, some automatic weapons and twelve air-to-ground rockets, which Dahi Baba, Musa Gawar and their technicians carefully removed, together with their launching racks. In Dahi Baba's workshop the powerful missiles were fitted on to portable platforms, each holding four; engineer Gawar and Dahi Baba got down to improvise a targeting and firing mechanism.

Ahmad Mazar and his group drew off the fuel and noted with satisfaction that there was enough to make three hundred petrol bombs – the principal guerrilla weapon against armoured vehicles.

Familiar with the Russian routine, Zafar now anticipated a fighter-bomber attack. With Jim's assistance he shifted the Chinese gun to the far side of the Pass. 'That copter was not alone – the one which fled must have worked out our position,' he told Jim, who agreed.

Forty minutes later, the MiGs roared in, to subject the evacuated site to a furious bombardment, unaware of the twin-barrels which tracked them during each bombing run from a completely different position. But Zafar was waiting for the last run, when the leading MiG would no longer turn, but dip a wing to knife between a pair of rock-faces on the way back to Jalalabad. 'The jets will be low on petrol,' he said, 'and they won't be able to come back and attack us even if they spot the gun.'

'Let me give it a try.' Jim spoke tensely.

Zafar got out of his seat, teasing, 'Aren't you supposed to be neutral, Jim?'

'The Russians aren't respecting my neutrality, damn it,' he replied, taking the controls. 'Besides, I'm getting a bit bored with you having all the fun.'

'Just don't miss,' Zafar said. 'Try to hit the last one in the line.'

Jim swung the barrels after the last jets as they streaked past at a distance of three hundred yards, 'to get the feel of the thing'. He waited until the last fighter-bomber had finished its strafing run and rolled into a tight turn to skim along a five-hundred-foot rock-face, then fired a short burst which ripped across wing and tail. The MiG spun round, cartwheeled into the cliff and exploded in a ball of fire.

'A fine finish,' he commented.

'That's not the finish,' Zafar countered, shaking his head. 'Now the Russians will send back the copters.'

'Why?'

'Because where we are now, the jets can't attack, and they very much want to destroy our gun.'

'Let's hitch on and move, then,' Jim said. 'You've only got one gun. It's a good idea to keep the Russkis guessing where it is.'

The AA-gun was moved eight hundred yards downhill and set up under a rocky overhang with a good view of the valley. Once again, Zafar was proved correct. The gunships came all right, but the gun position reported by the MiGs no longer tallied. The copters gave the evacuated cave and the surrounding underbrush a terrific banging and Zafar Ghazi bagged two more of them.

'I think I rather like this game of hide-and-seek,' Jim commented, after the last four copters had left at the double. 'Damn good sport.' He filled his pipe, lit it and added; 'Don't they ever get wiser?'

'The Russians?' Zafar chuckled, 'Never – so much the better for us. They do what they learned in the training camps and in the Party seminaries, even if it obviously no longer applies. If the Kremlin tells them, "You didn't lose three copters and a MiG over the Khawak," they'll believe it. In the USSR everyone is following someone else's orders and when one steps out of the line of command, he can easily become a deviationist, or a revisionist . . . It's a piece of luck for us: the regional commander does what the district commander tells him to do, who in turn obeys the orders of the commanding general in Kabul, who obeys his superior in Moscow, who – Allah merciful and benevolent – has no idea how to fight in a country like Afghanistan. No Red Army commander dares to improvise: for his idea might misfire and then he'll get shot . . . When his officers and sergeants fall, the little chaps give up, because they do not know what to do next . . . The Chinese say, Russia's Red Army is a huge, bellowing dragon with a tiny head and an even tinier brain.'

'So it seems,' the Englishman said. 'But that tiny brain can think up a mountain of malice as big as the Tirich Mir.'

HAJI KARAK AND HIS
FIGHTING GOAT

ALI GHAZI sent a rider to Acar Yarim, with a letter in which he invited the impetuous leader to the Khawak, to discuss a range of important matters, including joint future actions against Karmalist and Soviet objectives.

In actual fact, of course, Ali Ghazi and his companions did not think much of Yarim's attitude of reckless bravado. Even when crowned with success, Yarim's 'victories' were fringed with a gloomy sense of an unnecessary sacrifice having been made. He was, no doubt, an ardent patriot, relentless in his persecution of the enemy, but he was also paying too high a price for his achievements. By coordinating actions with Yarim, Ali Ghazi hoped he could eventually exert a restraining influence on him.

He also considered it extremely important to arrange a meeting with Haydar Chari, the one-time Afghan Army major who had deserted Karmal's tarnished regime to fight with the harassed peasants.

Chari believed that Babrak Karmal had dreams of becoming an Afghan Fidel Castro, although he had neither Castro's experience, nor his popularity; besides, dependent as he was on Soviet handouts, Castro still preserved much of his freedom of action, while Karmal could do little except what the commanding Red Army general and the Soviet Ambassador told him to do.

Haydar Chari's camp was in the Mommands range, the eastern extremity of which extended into Pakistan, close to the Khyber-Jalalabad-Kabul road, along which Chari and his *mojahedins* harassed the enemy incessantly and kept the refugee-routes open.

It was a long, gruelling trip from the Khawak to the Mommands and Ghazi opted to send Haji Karak to arrange the meeting with Chari. Karak was a sturdy hunter-trapper in his early fifties, who knew the province like the back of his hand; accustomed to long treks along difficult trails, he thought he could reach the Mommands in about ten days.

Carrying food, his Kalachnikov, a couple of grenades and the letter for Haydar Chari, he set off in the direction of Farajghan. He was accompanied by Meshu – his goat.

As the distinction 'haji' revealed, Karak had made the pilgrimage to Mecca, returning just as the Russian 'brothers' began their takeover in Afghanistan. He joined the *mojahedins* mostly because the majority of the able-bodied men in Silala had gone into the mountains and Karak had no wish to be singled out as one of Karmal's arse-lickers – the term used by the local guerrillas for those who resigned themselves to the new order, following the 'merchant of Afghan blood'.

Haji Karak was neither brave nor particularly enterprising, and he harboured a peculiar affection toward his old she-goat, Meshu; he would not be parted from her even when he went 'hunting' to 'bag' a few infidel invaders for the greater glory of Allah. Meshu had been with him for ten years, he said, and would never cause any trouble. Indeed, she followed Karak like a dog and apparently understood most of what he told her. She would even carry a pair of saddlebags with provisions and ammunition – and on the side she provided Karak with a pint of milk daily, and consequently with cheese as well.

It quite often happened that the *mojahedins* would have to go without food for a day or two, in the hills, and Haji Karak disliked walking on an empty stomach.

Naturally enough his companions teased him constantly: Meshu was Karak's 'wife', advising him on everything. If this was so, Meshu must have been a very gifted tactician for Haji Karak's Kalachnikov had netted him twenty Russians and fifteen Karmalist traitors within three months. He was not particularly proud of the fifteen Afghans. The Russian infidels were free game, but he disliked shooting his own people, even if – with the exception of mercenaries – they happened to be devoted 'arse-lickers': he would shoot to

119

wound, not to kill. Nonetheless, he railed against the Afghan soldiers who sided with the infidels. Karak thought that after the liberation such traitors should be enslaved, forced to work for the Afghans. He regarded Communism as a deadly poison, deadlier than the venom of the yellow-banded viper: it affected only the mind, leaving the hand free to rise against fathers, brothers, flag, country and Islam. 'The Communists cannot be good,' he reasoned, 'they have no faith and without faith a man is no better than the animals.'

Most of the raids in which Karak participated had taken place at night, when the utmost care and absolute silence were essential for success. At first Haji's companions threatened to slit Meshu's throat if she uttered so much as a feeble snort. In the end they learned that it was Meshu's bleating which lulled the enemy into a false sense of security.

This curious fact was discovered during a raid on a road-block manned by a dozen Russians and a platoon of Karmal-ists, supported by a tank and two armoured troop carriers. In order to get close enough for the surprise assault, the *mojahedins* were obliged to work their way across a patch of tangled underbrush at dead of night. Slithering like snakes, the men wormed themselves within easy distance for throwing grenades, followed by other explosives. They were unaware of the suspended tin cans with which the Russians had ringed the bushes, and a few bumped into the string and set off a noisy clanking.

Shouts and orders knifed into the silence. Troops poured from the carriers to take position along the road. Search-lights swept the bushes and the tank-turret slowly turned towards the site of the disturbance.

'We're in hot water now,' Haji Karak thought as a machine gun probed the thicket, snapping boughs and tearing leaves. Deprived of the element of surprise, the chance of success seemed lost and the *mojahedins* were about to beat a hasty retreat before the tank started lobbing shells.

Then, unexpectedly, Meshu blared a hearty bleat and the troops along the road burst out laughing.

'Chto takoi?' a coarse voice called from the tank turret. 'What's happening?'

120

'Nichevo,' another Russian replied reassuringly. 'It's only a stray goat.'

Meshu bleated again. Shouldering their weapons, the soldiers rose, relieved. More battery torches flashed through the shrubbery; clanking the tin cans a Russian corporal came over to investigate. He found Meshu but got his throat slit by Abi Safed, who seized his torch and headed for the road, flashing left and right to blind the sentries.

'Where's the goat?' one of them yelled and Safed replied with a grenade. It was followed by another which Karak tossed into the terrified mob on the road. Hurling grenades and firing incessantly the *mojahedins* surged forward and quickly overwhelmed the confused enemy. By the time the Russian gunners in the tank had re-positioned themselves, they could no longer open fire: friend or foe were locked in struggle and someone was throwing a Molotov Cocktail from the ditch. One of the troop carriers burst into flames and the tank commander thought it wise to flee. Chased by half a dozen guerrillas hurling bottles of petrol the tank put on speed and escaped just in time.

Pausing only to dispatch the wounded Russians and gather weapons and ammunition, the *mojahedins* melted into the dark hills. And now, as well as providing Haji Karak with milk and cheese, Meshu had established her reputation as a 'fighting goat'.

She could do many tricks. For one thing she hated having a tether round her hindleg and would perform incredible acrobatics to free herself – a habit which a few weeks later would earn her the honorary title of freedom fighter . . .

Having concluded his mission in the Mommands, Haji Karak was on his way back to the Khawak when a patrol of six Karmalists spotted him and his goat, trekking uphill on a open trail. At first, the sergeant in charge took Karak for a local peasant, but then he had another look through his field glasses, recognised the Kalachnikov and saw the grenades swinging from Karak's belt.

Firing warning shots, then shooting in earnest, the platoon gave Haji Karak the chase. He fled into a partly ruined hut that provided the only cover in the still snowbound neigh-

121

bourhood and started to fire back. The platoon took shelter in a depression. Though the *mojahedin* was alone, he carried grenades and the sergeant knew what a *kalachnikov* could do to exposed men. He decided to wait for dusk, then storm the hut and kill the rebel. There was a good reward for every rebel killed, but also for weapons seized and brought back to base. Payment in the Afghan Army was meagre, but the Russian rewards were generous, sometimes higher than a month's wages.

The Afghan patrol remained in the depression some two hundred yards from Karak's shelter, firing occasionally to keep the rebel occupied. Every now and then Haji Karak fired back, to remind the patrol that he was on the alert and they had better stay put.

Meshu bleated and Karak offered her a handful of weeds from between the stones. She browsed and Karak milked her, drank the lot, let loose a couple of slugs, then leaned back against the wall and rolled a cigarette.

The soldiers fired again. Some of the bullets whizzed into the roofless room. Meshu sprang into the air, and Haji drew her to the safe side, patted and spoke to her reassuringly. The Karmalists wasted a few more slugs; then the sergeant called out:

'Hey, Baba – have you got any bullets left?'

Haji Karak rose to a gap in the wall and shouted back;

'Come over and count them.'

'We only want your weapon to get our reward,' called the sergeant. 'Hand it over and we'll let you go home . . . Are we not brothers? We don't want to kill you. Let us have our reward and we'll let you go.'

'You'd get a better reward if you took my head back, too,' Karak replied. 'Traitors like you would sell their own mothers for money.'

'We are still brothers . . . '

'You are not brothers to honest Afghans, you're wretched traitors.'

'Let us prove our good faith.'

'How?'

'One of my men will come over unarmed. Go with him for

122

half a mile, then hand over the Kalachnikov without any bullets.'

'If one of your Karmal arse-lickers comes near me,' Karak yelled, 'I'll give him my rifle, all right, with the bullets – right in the belly.'

'It'll be dark soon.'

'Allah is great . . . I've got some grenades as well. You come and get me and we can all blow up together.'

But Haji Karak had no intention of blowing himself up. He was thinking how to get out of the trap. The sergeant was right: soon it would be dark and he wouldn't be able to stop the Karmalists from coming in.

'Why do you want to die?' the sergeant called again. 'Life is good.'

'Not in your jail, waiting for the rope.' He could hear the soldiers laughing.

'Baba . . . Tell us your name. We ought to write something on your headstone.'

'Haji Karak – from Silala,' Karak obliged. 'If I were you, I'd prefer to shoot Russians than Afghans.'

'A soldier must obey his orders, Haji.'

'You're not soldiers. You're godless marauders, like the traitor you serve.'

The sergeant let loose a short salvo. Karak shrugged and slid to the ground again.

Looking round the ruined hut, he spotted a few rusty nails and a length of wire and the idea came to him in a flash. 'The traitors know I'm alone,' he muttered to Meshu. 'It's no good – we'll have to get out of here and you'll have to help me.'

Meshu stared at him and bleated understandingly.

Karak checked the Kalachnikov and set it to single shots: there were enough cartridges in the magazine to hold the soldiers at bay for a while. Then he got down to his plan. With Meshu's help it might work.

Sheltering against random shots, he placed the gun in a jagged hole, fixing it with wire and nails so that it couldn't move, or drop. He attached a length of wire to the trigger, then tied the other end to Meshu's hindleg, which he first

123

wrapped in a bit of cloth in order not to hurt her. He patted the goat and spoke to her in a calm, soothing voice. 'I know you don't like it, but you must help me by shooting at the patrol while I try to get behind them. They think I'm alone, you see, so they won't expect any trouble from the rear . . . You keep them busy, Meshu.'

'Haji!' the sergeant yelled, 'give us the Kalachnikov and go home. The Russians pay good money for it.'

'I need a gun myself,' Karak yelled back. 'It's not safe in the hills without one.'

'We can give you a rifle.'

Meshu kicked out in disgust at the very idea, and the Kalachnikov in the wall fired. The sergeant swore and ducked. Karak sprang to the goat. 'Not yet, Meshu – wait till I've gone . . . Keep me covered and don't worry. I'll be back soon.'

Taking his grenades, he left the shelter and crawled away in a wide circle. He was barely twenty yards from the hut when Meshu fired a second round, then two more. The soldiers returned the fire and scared the goat into another fit of jumps and jerks. The automatic rifle in the wall blazed again and a wild exchange followed, while Haji Karak made his way behind the firing soldiers, whose attention was riveted to the hut.

He rose and flung a grenade, tore the safety pin of the second one and lobbed it before the first one had landed. The double blast blew the soldiers from the ditch like rag-dolls; Karak threw one more grenade for good measure, then charged into the smoke with pistol in hand.

He found one survivor whimpering on the ground with his left arm torn off at the elbow. The others were riddled with splinters and dead as doornails, including the sergeant, whose head lolled to one side.

Fetching a belt, Karak improvised a tourniquet round the stump of the wounded soldier's arm. 'Lalpura is only two hours away,' he told him. 'Perhaps you can make it to the first-aid station.'

'You weren't alone in the hut,' the Karmalist moaned almost reproachfully, as Karak gave him a drink of water. 'Who was firing at us?'

'Meshu – my goat,' Karak answered.

'Your goat . . . '

'Yes . . . She is a very clever goat.'

One automatic rifle, a short, mean-looking machine pistol, and the sergeant's automatic: Karak shouldered the lot, together with a bag of cartridges. The rest of the weapons had been much damaged by the explosions. 'You have any grenades?' he asked the wounded soldier, who weakly shook his head.

'No grenades? What sort of troops were you?' Karak shook his head disapprovingly.

He frisked the corpses and collected a handful of money, two watches, one good map, a compass and the sergeant's field glasses. He had another look at the wounded trooper's stump, reminded him to loosen the belt every now and then, gave him a can of water and helped him to his feet. 'This is all I can do for you . . . May Allah help you on your way.'

He returned to Meshu and patted her on the head.

'You're a great fighter, even though you are only a female,' he said kindly, then loaded some of his booty on her back. Meshu did not seem to mind.

When Ali Ghazi Khan learned of Meshu's accomplishments, he ordered that in future she should not only graze, but receive her daily ration of good cereals like every *mojahedin* and added with a smile: 'If we were in the army, I'd promote her to corporal.'

Ali Ghazi examined the small, snub-nosed machine pistol and pursed his lips. 'PM sixty-three, made in Poland,' he said angrily. 'They're already enslaved by the Soviets, yet they help the Red Army to rob others of their freedom.'

'The Poles can't do much with the Red Army sitting in their country,' engineer Musa Gawar reminded him, but Ghazi only spat. 'The Red Army is sitting in our country too . . . Men who do not dare to fight for their freedom are not men, but born slaves.'

He searched Karak's shoulder-bag and pulled out a couple of mags, short and long ones. 'Here is the one that goes with it,' he hefted the magazine. 'Fifteen bullets . . . There are others with forty cartridges.' He glanced at Haji and said with a wink; 'You got yourself a very good gun, Haji.'

Karak fingered his beard and looked levelly at Ghazi. 'You know it, you keep it,' he said after a brief consideration. 'I couldn't even aim that – thing.' The *mojahedins* laughed.

'With that *thing*,' Bazi Noor said chuckling, 'you don't have to aim, only pull the trigger. It sprays bullets like water.'

'I don't want to spray bullets, just put them where they belong,' Haji Karak replied, pushing the machine pistol back to Ali Ghazi.

A series of successful guerrilla operations and Karmalist-Soviet failures in the country began to convince even the apathetic masses that the cause of Afghan freedom was far from lost. The *mojahedin* ranks swelled as more and more young men from the cities and the beleaguered villages took to the hills. Army deserters would invariably join the *mojahedins* and the conscripts fled almost as soon as they received their call-up orders.

Later, however, desertion from the Afghan Army became less frequent: severe reprisals were meted out to the unfortunate relatives, even to the children of the deserters. Parents, wives and brothers of the 'traitors' would be hauled in for questioning, while the police ransacked their homes, looking for incriminating evidence and stealing whatever was of value and easily transportable. The deserters' relatives were thrown out of civil service jobs, universities and schools – losing pensions, scholarships and even medical benefits. Many would be detained for weeks, or jailed for an unspecified period. Those released were obliged to pay heavy 'fines', for which they were never given a receipt.

And it became general practice to 'back up' Afghan Army units in operational areas with a better equipped Soviet platoon or company, whose task was not so much to fight, as to prevent mass desertion.

When drug addiction became a growing problem among the Soviet troops, the *mojahedins* considered it an excellent development and a good weapon. Hashish and opium were permitted to fall into Russian hands in liberal quantities during every enemy raid or guerrilla withdrawal. Red Army addicts were screened and sent back to the USSR; the new-comers who replaced them were inexperienced beginners, easy to trap and kill. The corrupting of Russian soldiers became a popular pastime in the towns and villages, not only with drugs, but also through involving them in apparently favourable black-market deals. Junior officers of the Red Army who had amassed a small fortune in Afghanistan, would neither risk being killed in action, nor being caught by their superiors. If their loot was threatened, they would, in most cases, desert to the 'rebels' or flee to Pakistan. Red Army veterans arrested and sentenced to punishment camps in Russia would once again be replaced by greenhorns, to the delight of the seasoned *mojahedins.*

THE BASE AT CHARIKAR

ACAR YARIM arrived with an escort of ten riders. He was a lean, lithe man with a wedge-shaped face tapering to a sharp chin, his cheeks scarred with the wounds of some past skirmish. Acar Yarim liked to boast that his scars were reminders of a Russian machine-gun salvo, but his close friends murmured something about a brush with the police long before the invasion, when Yarim was not yet a local hero. He was a common bandit, then, holding up the cars and lorries of wealthy merchants – not to mention long-distance passenger buses around the Hindukush foothills. The scars were supposed to have been caused by a terrific wallop across the face from a policeman's bayonet. Even if that was true, they did not diminish Yarim's later standing as a patriot.

Jim found Yarim's face quite alarming, perhaps an effect of his dark, bushy brows, cultivated to grow upwards, lending the guerrilla's face a Mephistophelean ferocity. Jim thought he wouldn't much like to meet Acar Yarim in a dark alley.

Ali Ghazi, his brother Zafar and Ahmad Mazar welcomed Yarim at the entrance of the cave with a mug of hot tea. The four men embraced, shook hands, introduced their companions, then quickly began a lively discussion of Yarim's raid on the troop carriers in Dasht-i-Rewat.

Acar Yarim defended his action vehemently, saying that the loss of seventeen tracked vehicles had been a heavy blow to Karmal's army of traitors who had got only what they deserved. He swore he had acted in good faith, which was probably true. In any case he agreed that they should co-ordinate their actions in future by means of weekly dispatch riders between their respective camps. He also promised to refrain from action along the Banu-Rewat-Perwan trail, now established as Ghazi's territory. A rough map was drawn up to designate the operational areas of the two guerrilla groups.

Ali Ghazi presented Yarim with eight automatic rifles, some Russian pistols and thirty hand-grenades, after which the two leaders parted in good, brotherly spirit, happily anticipating their joint success against the common enemy.

The first step towards unity between at least two guerrilla groups had been made. Ali Ghazi Khan made up his mind to get the others in line, too, among them Safed Yar, a noted 'infidel hunter' with two hundred men fighting in the Koh-i-Baba range who, for all practical purposes, controlled the Irak and Unai Passes and caused ample trouble for the Afghan Army and its Soviet backers. The word 'mercy' was completely missing from Yar's vocabulary. He butchered his prisoners with such cruelty that troops sent after him would often prefer to desert than risk putting a foot on the territory of Safed Yar.

Haydar Chari, in the Mommands, had already agreed to a conference between all the important guerrilla leaders in Eastern Afghanistan. Zebak Vahan would not move from the 'horn' but he promised to keep the trails to China open and to do his best to supply his brother *mojahedins* with good weapons and ammunition.

Ali Ghazi was sure that once the four most important groups were in cooperation, the principal approaches of the capital would be controlled by the free Afghans from Ghazni in the south, to Doshi in the north-west. Forty thousand Russian invaders and fifteen thousand Karmalists would be exposed to constant harassment.

Even now, the hated enemy invader could claim little more than the principal cities and a few shaky miles of territory along the main roads, which their tanks could roam with relative safety – though not always.

The guerrillas knew that the Red Army garrisons in Afghanistan were relieved at three- to four-month intervals, usually long enough for them to become weary, jittery and disillusioned. As Safak Parakin rightly said, the newcomers could still be persuaded they would be fighting against American imperialist intruders, but the veteran garrisons knew better and could no longer be hoodwinked by their political officers. The exchange of troops was so arranged that the veterans and the new arrivals never encountered one another. The Russians have always been good at keeping secrets – especially unpleasant ones. And engineer Gawar had jokingly remarked, 'When the Russians announce good news, you have to deduct sixty per cent of it and consider half of what's left: when they talk of setbacks, you multiply their figures at least three times.'

Despite the loss of the troop carriers, Ali Ghazi did not discard the idea of raiding the base at Charikar – a most tempting target known to accommodate 3,000 troops, twenty helicopter gunships, twenty-four tanks, a transport battalion with sixty lorries and half-tracks, a company of engineers, ammunition and fuel dumps – all within an area of two square miles. Ghazi had a fairly accurate plan of the base drawn by Musa Gawar from the minaret of a nearby mosque, where he spent three days, helped by the local 'mullah'.

The base was situated on undulating ground at the north-eastern extremity of the Koh-i-Baba range, which ended near the base perimeter, with three-thousand foot elevations dominating the enemy installations. Captain Karatash suggested that the best way to attack would be from the southern side, despite the presence of a radar station on a low plateau. Having studied the scheme which Safak Parakin had helped to prepare, Ali Ghazi agreed. He wasn't even going to attempt to penetrate the perimeter, wired and mined with pillboxes and watch-towers at three-hundred-yard intervals. He wanted to seize the elevation and shell the base from there with mortars and rockets. He thought a few good hits on the buildings and the parked machines would be demoralising for the enemy and an uplifting experience for his *mojahedins* who would see the arrogant invaders on the defensive.

The parked copters, tanks and lorries would be exposed and vulnerable. The closest watch-towers and pillboxes could be attacked with grenades and petrol bombs. Some quarters and repair shops lay close enough to hit even with bazookas, and the element of surprise would be an important factor on the guerillas' side and might present unforeseen opportunities for additional destruction. The base had not yet been attacked and the Russians felt quite safe.

Lieutenant Yamrad suggested a fifteen-mile detour west of Charikar, where a ravine with a shallow stream ran beneath the Kabul-Doshi highway and where the guerrillas might safely pass to the southern side of the enemy base.

The idea of using the Perwan trail was debated and discarded: it was too heavily surveyed by the enemy. The only alternative was the snowy footpath along the eastern hills of the Hindukush range; longer by thirty miles, but also safer, and Acar Yarim knew the region well.

Faithful to the gentleman's agreement between the *mojahedins* and Safak Parakin, Ali Ghazi did not ask the former Red Army soldier to join the raid, although Parakin was familiar with the Soviet installations and would have been of certain help in selecting targets.

Taunting the lanky Englishman, Ahmad Mazar asked if he would come along to see some real action. Jim quietly declined. 'Any time your enemies venture into the Khawak I'll be ready to give you a hand,' he said. 'But I'm not going to go and look for the firing squad myself, Ahmad.'

Laughingly the big man accepted that.

Ghazi estimated that the trip would take eight to ten days by moving mostly at night and measured the rations accordingly. Mazar thought the highway should be crossed in the evening and the base attacked around 2 a.m. Musa Gawar reassured his companions that the base perimeter and the principal installations would be well illuminated. The Russians weren't too keen on darkness in Afghanistan.

Acar Yarim was duly informed of the planned attack and showed himself eager to take part. He wanted to take care of the radar station and the perimeter obstacles himself.

Ali Ghazi selected sixty men and Acar Yarim joined him with fifty more. He was fascinated by the twelve rockets which Dahi Baba and Gawar had fitted on to a wooden platform which could be raised or lowered, although actual aiming had to be done by guesswork.

'We'll see where the first one lands and turn the platform accordingly,' Musa Gawar explained.

The sophisticated targeting mechanism had remained onboard the crashed copter, but it could not have been used anyway without a 24-volt current.

They found the radar station and the two adjoining prefab quarters surrounded by wiremesh and trip-mines. Clad in white canvas, or wearing Russian snowsuits, the guerrillas covered a section of the perimeter with bales of hay and crossed safely into the compound.

The two guards were quickly dispatched, and advancing carefully the *mojahedins* occupied the overhang some six hundred feet above the base, and set up the mortars and the makeshift rocket-launching pads. Down below, the men of Zafar Ghazi and Acar Yarim waited near the base perimeter, spread out over three hundred yards, facing the closest pillbox and one of the watchtowers. The night was cloudless, with the crescent moon just above the skyline. Through the notched, converging gunport of the pillbox muffled laughter and merry voices filtered into the open.

Up on the overhang a Russian officer stepped out of the radar station, lit a cigarette, then walked off a few paces to pass water – his last act in the world of the living. Moving like a panther, Abi Safed pounced on him,: his long, curving knife glinted, the officer uttered a choked gurgle and dropped into the muddy snow. Safed snatched his belt and holster and went back to his place near the entrance. A few minutes later another Russian appeared in the open, called out, 'Piotr Safonov!' and was killed instantly by a shot from Safed.

Ali Ghazi fired into the nearest window and the attack began, with a dozen grenades hurled into the station and adjoining quarters. Fire and smoke erupted through the shattered doors and windows, and there were bewildered screams of anguish. Scantily-clad soldiers, dazed and terrified, staggered into the open and succumbed to a hail of bullets. Then the mortars opened up and the first rocket streaked towards a cluster of low buildings.

Down below, the *mojahedins* of Acar Yarim surged

forward and crossed into the base to attack the tower and pillbox with grenades and petrol bombs. Three hundred yards further, the second tower was toppled by Zafar Ghazi.

On the far side of the base, sirens wailed intermittently and the lighted windows went dark. Tank engines roared and muzzle-flashes illuminated their dark shapes. Musa Gawar's first rocket fell short of a building, but went on skidding in the snow, and exploded against the wall which at once caved in. The guerrillas cheered. Gawar raised the platform. The second rocket flew over the burning building and hit a block of officers' flats.

'Don't waste our rocket on the Russian wives and kids,' Ghazi shouted. 'Try to get the vehicle park!'

'That's what I'm trying to do!' Gawar shouted back, shifting the platform. 'It's very difficult, Ali.'

'It's your invention. Make it work.'

The third rocket knifed into a row of lorries and damaged a water tower at the same time. 'You're getting better,' Ghazi commented.

The mortars were effective from the beginning, and after a few wasted rounds the shells began to land right on the stationary copters and service vehicles. Sparse at first, the return fire began to gain strength, as the tanks rumbled closer firing at the elevation with the precision of skilled operators: their first salvo demolished the rest of the radar station with a dozen guerrillas inside, busy looting the dead Russians. One shell exploded twenty yards behind the mortars, wounded three men and enmeshed their writhing bodies in a wildly flying coil of barbed wire.

Down below, the pillbox had been silenced, but the guerrillas of Acar Yarim did not stop there. Howling 'Allah akhbar! Allah is great!' they charged the oncoming tanks with grenades, petrol bombs and bazookas. Zafar Ghazi could do little except try to pin down the Russian infantry behind the tanks.

Acar Yarim's furious charge was neither planned nor coordinated. Ali Ghazi considered it a senseless piece of bravado, but it distracted the tanks from the plateau and gave Gawar a short reprieve – enough to fire another twenty mortar shells and the rest of the rockets. By now, helicopters had joined the battle. Others, still on the ground with revolving rotors, were caught by the rockets. Another building exploded and a pile of fuel barrels began to burn.

In the field three tanks were in flames and Yarim's men were charging the others and the troop carriers with frenzied fury, facing at least three hundred Russians. Zafar Ghazi supported them as long as his ammunition lasted then, following the plan, began to withdraw.

The *mojahedins* of Acar Yarim were either completely enraged, or so overcome with hatred that the longing to kill the hated enemy swept aside fear, caution and every other consideration. They attacked the armoured vehicles even at the risk of burning alive. Four or five of them went down together, spun round, and fell to the snow spilling blood, but still they howled, 'Allah akhbar! Death to the invaders!' and those who could still move and raise themselves on one elbow, kept lobbing grenades and Molotov Cocktails. One man lost an arm, but pounced on his adversary, a tracked assault gun: the bottle exploded in his hand and turned him into a human torch. Still he dragged himself halfway on to the rear armour, smashed his second bottle over the air inlets and died, clinging to the blazing vehicle. Others threw themselves on the troop carriers starting raging fires wherever they succeeded. Guerrillas and Russians, many drenched with petrol and burning, ran amok, screaming, still firing, or rolling in the snow, locked in mortal combat. Not even Ali Ghazi Khan would ever have imagined that hatred should release so much self-sacrifice, heroism – or sheer madness. Yarim's kamikaze charge must have been a very unnerving experience for the Red Army troops: slowly but inexorably their coordinated action began to falter; the tanks and armoured carriers halted, changed direction and tried to back away from the howling madmen mobbing them like army ants.

Within a few minutes, eight tanks and sixteen troop carriers had been turned into blazing wrecks. Scores of Russians lay writhing or already dead in the red snow with uniforms burned, or still smouldering, while comrades shovelled snow over those still alive. One *mojahedin* with shattered legs lit his petrol bomb and flung it on to an uncoming tank before the track mashed him into the churned ground. Within yards, the tank stopped and burst into flames. Its crew fled into the open, only to be met by two human torches, burning from foot to turban, but still howling, 'Allah akhbar' and smashing bottles of petrol against the armour, setting fire to the screaming fugitives.

Another guerrilla sprang on to a half-track, flung himself on the gunner of the turret machine gun and dragged the Russian right under the tracked wheels.

Picking up as many weapons from the dead fighters and Russians as they could carry, the *mojahedins* withdrew, to assemble two miles west of the base. Miraculously, Acar Yarim was among the survivors: eleven men from a total of fifty-six. Nine men had died on the plateau and Zafar lost eighteen.

'My men were heroes,' Acar Yarim crowed. 'They all died like heroes and took many infidels with them.'

'It is true, but we need living fighters more than dead heroes,' Ali Ghazi reminded him grimly.

Acar Yarim was not moved by the sad loss. 'Let Allah's will be done. Our losses will be made good within a week, but the Russians and their tanks have a long way to come to Charikar and their next trip will be a bit different from when they first rolled into our country.'

THE FIRE ENGINE OF DAHI BABA

ACCORDING TO the still discernible date on the undercarriage, the derelict, horse-drawn fire engine had been around since 1889 and any museum would probably have been glad to accommodate it. It had been discovered by Zafar Ghazi and engineer Gawar in a shed in Dasht-i-Rewat and having checked the one-ton cistern, Gawar suggested that the veteran was in good enough shape for transporting or storing petrol and its twin faucets would make it easy to fill bottles and canisters.

After mending a pair of broken wheels, the *mojahedins* drove the pump to Dahi Baba's workshop for an overhaul. The hoses were missing, some cracks and holes had to be mended, or plugged, but the moment Jim saw it the idea hit him: something designed to spray water on a fire, could easily be used for spraying oil to start fire – or rather raise an inferno. He mentioned it to Dahi Baba whose eyes lit up with interest; Musa Gawar burst out laughing and Ali Ghazi grasped the Englishman by the shoulders and gave him a kiss on both cheeks.

'Jim, your head is worth its weight in gold,' he boomed.

'I just hope you won't be able to weigh it in the foreseeable future.'

For the next couple of days Dahi Baba's workshop buzzed with activity. Carpenters and fitters changed worn and decayed parts, and repaired the twin-handled pump, the ancient pistons and outlets.

Masquerading as ordinary farmers taking cheese and vegetables to the town market, three unarmed guerrillas drove a cart to Jalalabad to borrow a length of waterhose from the irrigation project. They returned with a thirty-yard, three-inch wide hose, which Dahi Baba fitted with the proper sockets, joints and a copper nozzle. The moving parts were greased and run in until everything functioned smoothly. The pump was tested with water. Worked by four men at each handle, it shot an eighty-foot spray across the valley.

The cistern was filled to capacity with a mixture of petrol and oil and hauled on to a sheltered overhang fifty feet above where the road ran hemmed in between towering rock-faces; they were half way between the Pass and the meeting of the Panjshir and Karan rivers. The men of the Khawak were ready to receive any enemy intruder with 'real hell', as Jim put it when he inspected the site.

It was late May that the refitted fire engine received its 'baptism by fire' and neither the *mojahedins* nor the Russians ever forgot it.

With the winter over, the Karmalists and their Soviet 'advisers' – some twelve hundred of them – embarked on a massive offensive against the 'bandits of the Panjshir valley'. The three-pronged attack involved nearly four thousand men, thirty tanks and armoured cars, supported by MiGs and twenty helicopter gunships.

The ponderous sweep into the Khawak began with the landing of a copter-borne Soviet assault platoon, which skilfully seized two small bridges – unprevented by the guerrillas – and established a strong perimeter. Obeying Ghazi's orders, the *mojahedins* stayed out of sight, and allowed a group of engineers to reinforce the old stone bridges with a steel scaffold for the transit of light tanks. 'We don't want only their men, but the tanks and artillery,' Ali calmed his impatient fighters, many of whom had the enemy in plain view and found it increasingly difficult to resist temptation. 'Let them come higher up.' Swearing between their teeth, the guerrillas obeyed.

At the same time, in the Anjuman, a few miles north of the river junction, troops were landing on a small plateau two miles east of the Khawak, while the tanks, armoured carriers and infantry advanced along the roads to Rewat and Banu.

The Russian paratroop landing on the Khawak-Banu road began more like a comic opera than an assault. Caught by a sudden upcurrent, eight paratroopers were lifted straight into Zafar Ghazi's position and captured on landing. Ahmad Mazar wanted to kick them into the ravine head first, others opted for hanging, some were all for crucifying the infidels: in fact it was the Englishman who saved their lives – through a 'hilarious idea' which made Mazar and Zafar Ghazi rock with laughter. Jim knew that no plea or reasoning would ever save the captives, so he banked on the guerrillas' fondness for playing jokes on the enemy. Still chuckling, Zafar Ghazi strolled to the terrified group, greeted the prisoners with a friendly, ' "kak diela?" '– 'how are you?' and with the student Muharrem Kunduz interpreting, he casually informed the Russians where their comrades were gathered and that they were free to return to them. Completely baffled, the paratroopers exchanged worried glances, murmured between themselves, and stared at the *partizanskis* who looked at them with encouraging smiles; their bewilderment became pure stupidity when, taking his map of the area, Ghazi showed a Russian corporal which footpath to take.

'But you must change into Afghan clothes and wear turbans,' Kunduz told them seriously. 'We have armed men posted along the trail and they hate the sight of Soviet uniforms . . . It's only for your own good.' And prodded by the guerrillas, the terrified Red Army men stripped and put on the tribal habits they were offered. Guffawing, some of Mazar's men went to fetch a bag of shorn goat hair and glue and each paratrooper received a fierce-looking moustache and bushy beard. 'We need your submachine guns, but we can give you some good local weapons,' Kunduz interpreted for Ghazi, while Mazar began distributing vintage shotguns with three cartridges for each, saying; 'You shouldn't walk around in the hills without a weapon. There are bears and wolves . . . Sometimes even leopards . . . '

The bearded, beturbaned Russians now looked utterly miserable: they just could not work out what Ghazi was up to. Some held the shotguns like broomsticks, others let them drop, a few shrank away as if they were being offered a bomb.

'It's a good gun,' Mazar hung it on the shoulder of a stiff-limbed Russian. 'Boom, boom – *ochin haraso* – very good.'

Zafar Ghazi showed the confused group the way. 'Russki comrades down there,' he chuckled, wiping away tears. ' "Idite! Go! "Dosvidanie" '. His 'see you later' made the *mojahedins* laugh even harder. 'It gives you a lift before battle,' Zafar Ghazi said chuckling. 'How do they look, Jim?'

'Like a group of pilgrims to Mecca,' the Englishman answered, himself rocking with laugher. But inside he was glad that the Russians had not been slaughtered. 'You see? it *was* more fun, than shooting them.'

Ahmad Mazar chuckled. 'Oh, they'll be back. We can shoot them later.'

'But the Russians saw our Chinese gun,' said Kunduz.

'And we are going to move it further uphill,' Zafar Ghazi replied cheerfully. 'The enemy will spend a lot of ammunition on the rocks round here.' Then, speaking to the Englishman, he added, 'You ought to get back to Ali, Jim.'

The three-pronged offensive began with artillery bombardment along the Banu road and vicious MiG strikes against suspected guerrilla positions north of Rewat. The only mistake the Russians made was the landing of four companies of Karmalists between Ali Ghazi's position and the encampment of Captain Karatash in the Anjuman Pass. The ex-Afghan Army officer instantly realised what a godsend he had and resorted to a clever ruse. Putting on their uniforms, the men of Karatash hurried after the advancing government detachment, whose commander mistook them for newly landed reinforcements. He halted to wait for the newcomers, who quickly surrounded and disarmed the Karmalists, and herded them into a cave to remain there for the duration of the battle. A handful of soldiers wanted to join the *mojahedins*. Having spoken to Ali Ghazi through the walkie-talkie, Karatash accepted them and marched off to join the defenders of the Banu road where a furious battle was in progress.

The column of armour and trucks on the southern, Rewat side sector, droned uphill with machine guns and cannons blazing incessantly, raking the underbrush round every bend, blasting the rock-strewn slopes and the visible caves and crevasses. They made a great deal of noise, but did no damage to the defenders who still refused to reveal themselves. Ali Ghazi was not particularly worried about the enemy advance across the reinforced bridges, quite close to Dahi Baba's caves: they were rolling into a fiery trap and it was quite impossible for the infantry to leave the road and charge the higher ground over the exposed slopes.

On the western side of the Khawak the situation seemed more serious where Soviet paratroops and an Afghan Army battalion were slowly gaining ground. Making good use of their superior position, Zafar Ghazi, Muharrem Kunduz and some hundred and eighty *mojahedins* resisted fiercely with machine guns, automatic rifles, grenades, arrow-borne dynamite and the Chinese rapid-fire gun. Here, for the first time, the Russians also used flame-throwers, mounted on armoured cars, and forced the guerrillas to come out of some of the crevasses.

'Just wait – we'll fry you, too,' Muharrem Kunduz swore, while Zafar concentrated his fire on the armoured carriers and light tanks and managed to knock out two of the dangerous vehicles, before a swarm of attacking copters forced him to shift aim. With Kunduz and three men assisting him, Zafar Ghazi put up a terrific fight, smashed the cockpit of the leading gunship and turned the one behind it into a fiery ball; he switched back towards the armour, blasting tracked wheels, turret machine guns, tyres, jeeps and scores of infantry, obliging the enemy to halt and back into sheltered caves along the road. The arrival of Captain Karatash and his well-equipped troops immediately improved the situation. The bazookas put four tanks and armoured cars out of action and momentarily halted the advance. Relieved from the task of holding the road as well, Zafar Ghazi resumed fighting the copters, and sent another gunship into the ravine below before a salvo of four rockets landed nearby. Hit by fragments in the head and chest, Zafar died instantly. Muharrem Kunduz, himself seriously wounded, gathered a few men and managed to push the slightly damaged gun deeper into the cave before he, too, collapsed and died a few minutes later.

Using the walkie-talkie, Ali Ghazi had been in contact with Captain Karatash and Ahmad Mazar. His brother, however, was beyond range and he learned of Zafar's death only after the battle.

Sheltering in a small, but convenient crevasse some hundred yards from Dahi Baba's workshop, Jim tried to make himself useful by snap-shooting with dynamite-tipped arrows towards the close-flying copters, swearing between his teeth whenever the fuses were too short or too long. Having wasted half a dozen shots he blasted the tail rotor of a copter which spun crazily away and crashed on top of an Afghan army truck labouring uphill, setting it on fire and causing quite a panic along the road. Jim decided that dynamite was good enough against ground targets, but not fast-moving objects such as planes and copters which needed a perfectly-timed explosion.

It was at this point that the southern prong of the enemy advance reached the point where the road was hemmed in between high rock-faces, where the veteran fire engine waited for its chance. It had been set up under a sheltering overhang, properly camouflaged, with the hose run out to the ledge of the precipice where engineer Gawar and Bazi Noor lay in tense anticipation. Following Ali's plan, the southern convoy had not been fired on. Gawar permitted some five hundred infantry to pass unhindered; then, from the caves of Dahi Baba, rose a red Very-light, a thunderous blast, followed by the muffled rumble of cascading earth and stone, announcing that a section of the road was now buried under the dynamite-fired landslide.

The ancient fire engine, converted into 'the greatest flame-thrower in the history of warfare' had probably brought about the quickest and most complete destruction of a Red Army column in the entire history of the Soviet Armed Forces. The road where the troops were marching, the soldiers themselves, tanks, armoured cars, lorries laden with troops and ammunition, and tracked vehicles towing artillery were drenched with a mixture of petrol and oil. Instantly realising what was about to happen, the vehicles halted, and crews, gunners, driver and troops scattered in a desperate

141

attempt to escape from the volatile area, where they could not even shoot. Leaving behind weapons, baggage and other equipment, maddened with fear, the panicking men dropped, skidded, slithered and rolled down the rugged slope to the river. A single grenade arched after them and the petrol-sodden road billowed into a roaring inferno with fifty-foot tongues of flame leaping in every direction. The initial blast was so intense that it also killed half a dozen *mojahedins* who had been careless enough to perch above the convoy, peering down to watch what happened.

Musa Gawar and Bazi Noor were themselves singed and blown backwards, and the slope beneath the nozzle of the nose was soaked as well. The fire spread upwards, caught hold of the hose, and raced along its entire length towards the pump, where the tank still contained a good measure of fuel. Noor, Gawar and their companions fled for their lives. An instant later the fire engine became engulfed, then exploded with a tremendous burst of flame – a mishap that had not been foreseen by Gawar.

Down below, the ammunition lorries exploded one after another, blasting more of the road, bringing down thousands of tons of rocks and earth. From the caves of Dahi Baba, Jim, Ali Ghazi, and Safak Parakin had a good view of the holocaust. Although the vehicles were blanketed with fire and smoke, they could see hundreds of screaming, staggering human torches collapsing up on the precipice, rolling into the river like fireballs, dead, or dying. On the far side of the land-slide a few surviving vehicles were backing away, still harassed by the guerrillas and suffering more losses.

The collapse of the southern prong freed the *mojahedins* from that sector and they hurried over to the far side of the Khawak where the Russian paras and the decimated Afghan Army battalion were still trying to force the road under the protection of gunships. The Chinese gun was still out of action: although Dahi Baba had already fixed the slight damage, there was no one to handle it – a mistake made by the fallen Zafar Ghazi, who, in his fondness for his beloved weapon, had kept putting off the idea of training others.

Only engineer Musa Gawar, Safar Parakin and Jim knew

142

how to handle the rapid-fire gun properly. Gawar was back in the caves being treated for burns. Maintaining the gentleman's agreement between them, Ali Ghazi did not want to ask Parakin to fire at his former comrades. With his 'neutrality' already in shreds, Jim took the seat behind the twin barrels, just in time to rip along the fuselage of a close flying MiG and send it rolling into the hillside. This unexpected development scared the rest of the squadron and the copters away from the restricted airspace around the Khawak. After the hasty withdrawal of the Air Force, the enemy ground attack began to lose impetus, then halted altogether.

When the news of the fiery disaster in the southern sector reached the paratroops, they began to withdraw towards Banu. Out of range of the AA-guns, the MiGs and copters returned to cover their retreat. The much-decimated Afghan Army battalion had long since fled the area and the Russians performed such a good fighting withdrawal that Ali Ghazi thought it was not worth the trouble to pursue them.

Of the four thousand troops involved in the ill-fated strike, only some seventeen hundred survived, including the captured Afghan detachment, which Ghazi later released. The Russians lost sixty per cent of their deployed armour and transports and almost all the artillery, which never had a chance to fire a single shell. Four field guns were salvaged and later repaired by Dahi Baba and Gawar, but none had any ammunition left. The ammo trucks had all gone up in the holocaust.

There was no merry celebration of the significant victory. The victors mourned their dead companions, one hundred and eighty *mojahedins*, among them Zafar Ghazi, Muharrem Kunduz, Ali Jamrad and Lieutenant Karam, who had died in the defence of the Khawak and the camp.

Their sacrifice had not been in vain.

The collapsed offensive was to be the last enemy attempt to eliminate the rebels from the Anjuman range with ground forces.

143

THE BLOWTORCH

LED BY Ashraf Vahan, one of Zebak's younger brothers, a caravan of twenty riders arrived from the 'horn', bringing Zebak's greetings to Ali Ghazi with six hundred rounds of ammunition for the Chinese gun, two crates of mortar shells, hand-grenades and an assortment of small arms. There were also two hundred old German Mannlicher rifle-barrels for Dahi Baba which Zebak must have got from the Chinese, and which looked as if they'd been around since the Boxer Rebellion. The old man was delighted. The barrels were of high-quality steel and he wanted to turn them into handy machine pistols to fire explosive bullets, designed by engineer Gawar.

Dahi Baba needed tungsten-tipped knives for his lathe-bench and reliable springs for the firing mechanism. Ahmad Mazar and Abi Safed set out on the mule ride to Doshi, where Mazar wanted to see Amer Sarhan, a fellow blacksmith and old friend of his who had a number of precious tools, including the coveted knives.

Unarmed, and carrying four sacks of cheese 'for sale in the market', the two men passed the Karmalist road blocks and arrived safely at Sarhan's workshop, only to learn that the master had been arrested by the police the evening before for 'associating with counter-revolutionary rebels' – a charge which foreboded a prolonged absence. In the ransacked workshop, Mazar and Safed found only two young brothers, Jamin and Imran Kuslakh, mere apprentices. Smith Sarhan's arrest was bad news, but Mazar still got what Dahi Baba wanted: twelve tungsten-tipped knives and sixty coil springs which the boys recovered from a hollow in the adjoining junkyard, plus a tinful of detonators which Sarhan had manufactured for home-made land mines.

Situated on the highway to the USSR, Doshi was fully controlled by the Russians – an unhealthy place, which Mazar wanted to leave the same evening. He decided to take a selection of important tools and four small tubes of oxyacetylene, always needed, but hard to obtain – saying that Amer Sarhan wouldn't be around for a while to use them anyway.

The Kuslakh brothers wanted to join Mazar and Safed and were accepted. Laden with tools and welding equipment the four could not pass the Karmalist check points; the boys knew a way across the gardens and orchards, but it wasn't for riders. After a short discussion, it was agreed that Imran should take the mules outside town and wait in an old quarry, while Jamin guided Mazar and Abi Safed safely past the check points, with their burden.

Leading the mules, Imran set off and the others settled down in the workshop to wait for dusk. It was already getting dark when a thunderous explosion shook the walls and windows. From the junkyard a swiftly rising pillar of smoke and leaping flames were visible in the northern section of Doshi. Moments later wild shooting burst out and lasted for several minutes, dotted with the sporadic explosions of grenades. Despite the curfew, people were running down the street, shouting, yelling, asking questions: a pair of Afghan Army armoured cars hurried towards the scene of the action. Jamin went to see what had happened. He ran back within fifteen minutes, panting hard. 'The *mojahedins* of Acar Yarim have blown up the regional office of the 'Parcham' Party with all the Communists inside,' he gasped excitedly. 'They say fifteen Karmalist traitors were killed and four big Party men from Russia.'

Ahmad Mazar shook his head. 'No big Party men from Russia would be staying in Doshi,' he said. The people were always ready to add a few dead Russians to the victims of every guerrilla raid. As it turned out later, the 'four big party men from Russia' were agronomists from a 'Sovhoz' state farm across the border, and they were not dead, only treated for superficial wounds and shock.

'Perhaps they're shocked enough to pack up and go

home,' said Ahmad Mazar, and Abi Safed added glumly; 'I only like them when they go home in wooden boxes.'

In any event, the raid – in which some twenty Karmalists perished – bore the trademark of Acar Yarim. Under the circumstances this was not happy news. The destruction of the much despised Party Headquarters brought troops and tanks into town. Soviet and Afghan armour rapidly occupied the squares and principal junctions, while police and army patrols began to search for the dispersed rebels believed to be still in town. The search parties meant business. They went from street to street and from house to house, and loud-speakers blared orders for the inhabitants to return home within fifteen minutes and remain indoors.

'It's impossible to leave now,' Mazar grunted as a Red Army tank churned round the corner, stopped and backed on to the pavement, blocking half the narrow street and almost touching the derelict stone wall of the workshop yard. Twenty yards further down the street an Afghan Army lorry with a machine gun took up position, with a platoon of soldiers in attendance.

'That's where we should be going,' said Jamin Kuslakh, pointing towards a large hole in a garden wall on the far side of the street.

'We can't cross the street with all those soldiers watching,' Mazar commented. 'It'll get dark later.'

'We can't wait until the police arrive to search the work-shop,' Jamin argued.

'Well, they haven't come yet.'

But when evening fell a powerful searchlight mounted on the truck illuminated the entire length of the street. The Russian tank, too, had turned on its headlights.

The Red Army was learning it the hard way: the invasion of Afghanistan was not the customary pushover, as Hungary, or Czechoslovakia had been, where the ruthless savagery of a few hundred tanks and artillery had quickly eliminated organised opposition. It was not so easy to be an invader in a country like Afghanistan – and a godless invader at that; not even in a small township like Doshi, which the infidels occupied and held in a steel grip as a matter of principle. Situated on the Kabul-USSR highway, Doshi was only one of a dozen places along the important supply route garrisoned by the Red Army and their Karmalist servants.

The local people ignored the unbelievers and their vehicles – at least on the surface. They walked sullenly past the enemy with averted eyes, and the friendliest Russian attempt to fraternise met only stony indifference if not open hostility. Soldiers who went shopping were not served, or only with reluctance and after a long wait. The very air the invaders were compelled to breathe seemed charged with enmity and in the darkness of the night loomed keen ears, sharp eyes and sharper daggers: whether they were really there or not, the alien invaders felt them anyway. Wherever they were stationed, assassins were at large – 'counter-revolutionary rebels' or simply bereaved men who had lost their loved ones to the invaders and were looking for revenge; desperate men, always ready to kill a careless invader with a length of rope, a curving dagger or an axe, striking from the darkness.

No, Afghanistan was not an easy country to conquer, much less to hold. Its people were accustomed to hardship. Life had always been hard, but the Russian invasion made it even harder. The incessant fighting in the rural regions, the systematic Soviet destruction of 'rebel' villages, cornfields and livestock cut the regular supply of food and made many important commodities scarce, available only on the black market. Fewer and fewer farmer would risk the dangerous roads; the behaviour of the invaders was wholly unpredictable. It frequently happened that – frustrated in some of their designs in the mountains – the Russian pilots simply swept down on caravans of farmers, gunning down men, mules and carts. Constantly harassed by the *mojahedins* the Russians saw armed rebels everywhere and would consider a group of fifteen Afghans a band of 'partisans' regardless of place or circumstance.

They machine-gunned funeral processions, weddings, groups of shepherds sitting round the campfire – a gunship blasted a peasant family carting a load of stove-pipes, which

147

the Russian gunner mistook for bazookas. A squadron of MiGs attacked and decimated a Karmalist Army regiment camping in the hills. A small misunderstanding. '*Nichevo* – nothing . . . ' There were still enough Afghans left.

The street was alive with unpleasant noises.

Brutal orders. Angry shouts and protests. Vicious arguments. Women crying hysterically. Soldiers cursing. Near the intersection, half a dozen suspects were being pushed and dragged towards the Afghan Army lorry, rifle-butted up the short ladder. Yelling policemen tried to separate clinging wives and sobbing children from their menfolk and when it proved too difficult they simply pushed woman and child on to the truck too. More people spilled out on to the street shouting and throwing stones and dung at the soldiers and police. A sergeant fired into the air, but his show of authority did not impress the furious mob. More stones flew and some landed where it hurt. The lieutenant of the Afghan Army platoon sprang to the mounted machine gun and fired a short burst into the pavement a few yards ahead of the throng. The ricochets wounded several men. The crowd faltered and was still.

The Russian tank-crew did not move, but stayed beneath the closed hatches, feeling uneasy, unsafe, despite the sixty tons of armour and guns protecting them.

Squatting behind the low, barred window of the workshop, Ahmad Mazar and Jamin Kuslakh observed the tank and the lorry further down the road. Jamin thought the tank was so large and heavy that it could probably destroy Doshi simply by driving through the houses. He had seen a tank like that crushing a three-storey house with a group of *mojahedins* inside. The floors came down and the tank churned debris and bodies into a flattened mass of pulverised masonry.

'The poor fellows are going to end up in the "Charkhi" too,' Abi Safed commented glumly, referring to Kabul's infamous prison, where the Karmalists had over fifty thousand opponents of Communism detained. 'That's the place we ought to blow up one of these days.'

'Yes, but right now we could do with a good diversion right here,' said Mazar.

Squatting with his back against the wall, smoking, Abi Safed shrugged and said, 'Why not blow up the tank?'

'Oh yes? What with?'

Jamin cut in excitedly. 'With the blowtorch mixture; Acetylene explodes just like that!'

Mazar's face lit up. 'Masallah, you're quite right,' he complimented the boy. 'Why not?'

He liked the idea. 'Even if we only damage the tank it'll create enough diversion for us to get to the hole in the wall . . . Perhaps even the prisoners might manage to escape.'

He studied the exhaust system's twin silencers and the grilled vents of the air inlet. 'Fetch another pair of hoses,' he told Jamin. 'We have to put gas into the exhaust and the intake.'

With Safed's help he lugged the blowtorch equipment on its wheels into the junk-strewn yard, fastened the nozzles to a pair of ten-foot canes and manoeuvered them into the intake-exhaust openings which Jamin then sealed with oily rags as best he could.

Mazar surveyed their work with satisfaction, turned on the twin tubes and listened for a few seconds to the soft hissing sound of the volatile mixture pouring into the tank. 'Now let's get away from here.' He beckoned to his companions, and the trio withdrew to the furthest part of the workshop and squatted down behind a lathe-bench.

'The Russians will smell the gas and come out,' Abi Safed, and Jamin added, 'Unless they blow up first . . . If one of them smokes, or strikes a match, or if the driver turns on the engine . . . ' He was silent, then said anxiously: 'Suppose the workshop blows up as well . . . The tank must be full of shells . . . Fifteen yards isn't much when a tank blows up.'

All of a sudden the turret hatch was flung open and loud voices could be heard. 'They've noticed something's wrong,' said Jamin, and the next instant the whining sound of the starter was followed by a violent explosion. Rushing to the low window the culprits saw a tongue of blue-white flame erupt from the turret: the exhaust system blew from the armour and spiralled across the street: the wall of the yard collapsed and the roof above them sagged, showering debris on to the floor. Out in the street police and soldiers came running. A Jeep arrived with a Soviet officer, yelling ' "*Partizanski!*" ' over and over, and waving his pistol.

'Let's go!' Mazar said, shouldering a cylinder of oxygen while Safed took the acetylene. Jamin grabbed the bag of tools. 'This way!'

They peered out at the street and saw a gratifying turmoil: the tank was burning fiercely, with muffled explosions inside. 'Stand back! It's going to blow up!' the Afghan Army sergeant shouted. The soldiers scattered, running for cover. Hauling their burden, the three *mojahedins* crossed the street and raced towards the gap in the wall thirty yards ahead. 'Halt!' a yell challenged them and a shot rang out: the next instant a blinding blast almost blew them across the hole into a muddy garden. The massive turret of the tank lifted, tilted and slipped on to the pavement. Leaping, twenty-foot flames singed the nearby trees and a cloud of smoke blanketed the street. The shells began to explode. Tracers drew lazy circles above the houses. Another blast ripped open the fuel tank, spilling diesel, already burning, to flow down the street like lava, setting fire to wooden fences, parked carts and electricity poles.

Walking in soft earth and mud, Mazar and his companions reached a narrow canal, waded across and climbed over low walls. Eventually they reached a deserted alley and headed eastward to the quarry where Imran waited with the mules.

Looking back they could see the flames leaping high above the roofs of Doshi. The workshop was on fire, and so were a dozen neighbouring houses. Still more explosions rumbled in the distance. 'I'm sure the prisoners in the lorry managed to escape,' Jamin said, then added sadly: 'The workshop is destroyed, as well . . . But when the *mojahedins* liberate our country, we'll work for Master Sarhan without pay, until we've rebuilt his workshop.'

Mazar slapped him on the shoulder. 'When we liberate Afghanistan, you'll have plenty of helping hands, Jamin.'

'I think all the Russians in the tank died,' said the boy.

'I think so, too,' said Mazar, 'but the tank is more important.'

'The Russians have got plenty of tanks,' Abi Safed pointed out.

'They're also losing a great many,' Mazar replied. 'And they don't grow on trees.'

Safely outside Doshi, climbing a trail to a low hill, they ran into a group of guerrillas watching the fires in the town: the men of Acar Yarim – much astonished.

'What were *you* doing in Doshi?' Yarim asked, embracing Mazar. 'Doshi and Banu are our territory – Ghazi put it on the map himself.'

Ahmad Mazar explained to him the nature of their 'infringement of rights' and Yarim boomed: 'And you've blown up a tank . . . We blasted their party gathering.' He burst out laughing. 'What a great evening for Karmal!'

From his shoulder bag he took a carefully folded sheet of paper and handed it to Mazar. 'Here, this will interest Ali Ghazi . . . A Russian directive to the Afghan comrades . . . Most interesting. It seems that the *mojahedins* of Badakshan and Afghan Turkestan are setting a most disturbing example to the Uzbeks and Tajiks in the USSR. The Kremlin is already worrying about their frontier dwellers becoming contaminated with revolutionary ideas.'

ALISTER, NATALIE
AND THEIR FLYING BOMBS

A RIDER came from the Mommands with a letter for Ali
Ghazi Khan. He read it, had a few words with the messenger,
and consulted with Ahmad Mazar, engineer Musa Gawar
and Dahi Baba. Then he sent for Jim and told him mildly;
'Jim, my friend, you ought to go to the Mommands with Musa
Gawar to meet the British couple I mentioned to you before.'

'You mean the ones who invented something to frig the
copters with?' Jim asked. 'Are they still around?'

'In Haydar Chari's camp – giving the helicopters a rough
time, Jim.'

'They must be crazy.'

Ghazi laughed softly. 'Do you consider yourself crazy?'

Jim snorted. 'Of course I do. I should have been back in
England long ago, playing golf in Richmond, instead of
Russian roulette in the Khawak . . . What are those two
blessing the Russian copters with? Alister and Natalie, if I
remember rightly, aren't they?'

'Yes – they're building some sort of flying bombs,' Ghazi
replied. 'Very effective against copters, trucks, fuel tankers
and stationary aircraft. Haydar Chari wants us to see the
weapon in action and perhaps introduce it ourselves.'

'Flying bombs . . . ' Jim couldn't quite visualise them. The
term made him think of the German V-1 drone of World War
Two – how could anyone manufacture something like that in
the Afghan mountains, or in Peshawar?

Then Haydar Chari's rider cut in, explaining in broken
English: 'Small aeroplanes with engines – flying very fast
. . . No copter, or truck can escape it . . . Hits target and
blows up.'

'Have you seen it yourself?' Jim asked him.

'Yes, I have.'

Jim got the idea. His compatriots were building model aeroplanes fitted with some kind of explosive charge. Radio controlled. What a brilliant idea!

'Haydar Chari calls them the *mojahedin* Air Force,' Ghazi said grinningly. 'Who knows? It may be true.'

'And an air force very difficult to shoot down,' Jim said. 'When do you want me to leave Ali?'

'Tonight. You'll be with Haydar in four days – if Allah so wills.'

'And Brezhnev,' Jim added good humouredly.

He met his companions in one of Haydar Chari's camps in the Mommands – only six miles from the border – and greeted Alister and Natalie with a cheerful; 'Hallo there! Up till now I thought I was the only crazy Brit in the region, but I'm glad to see there are others too.'

'Three's a better number,' Alister replied with a grin. They shook hands. As they talked, Jim found the couple so distinctly intellectual that he could not help wondering what they were doing in the Afghan wilderness in the first place. They came from Bristol. Alister, probably in his early forties, was tall and lean, with a high forehead and curly light brown hair. He wore light, gold-rimmed glasses. Natalie wore sun-specs and had her blonde hair piled up on top of her head. She had a slightly upturned nose, blue eyes and a prim mouth and was perhaps thirty-two. Both were clad in impeccable safari-style suits and boots.

'Well, this calls for a celebration,' said Alister, taking a leather-bound canteen from his saddlebag. 'Scotch,' he said conspiratorially, 'original Haig – pretty scarce in these parts.' Unscrewing the cup, he filled and offered it to Jim. 'Cheers.'

'Cheers.'

He slid down on to a bundle of rugs by the small campfire, shielded with boulders.

'So, how long have you been a *mojahedin*, Jim?' Natalie asked, smiling.

'Over a year now.'

'Actually *fighting* the Russians?'

'Rather kicking the Red Army in the shinbone,' he replied with a grin. 'If that can be called fighting.'

'As long as the kick hurts,' said Alister.

'I've tried my best.'

'And you're still trying, we hear,' Natalie added. 'You're quite famous in Afghanistan, you know.'

'You can't complain either, Natalie. How are your flying bombs coming along?'

'Fine,' said Alister. 'Fine, I think. We hope they'll give the Afghans a bit of a breather, and perhaps give the Soviet High Command a few sleepless nights. I wish we could have a factory for them.'

Later, over a dinner of roast lamb and rice in the company of Haydar Chari and some of his closest companions, Jim learned that Alister and Natalie were veteran 'Orientals', having left England in 1965 to work for ICI in Dacca.

'I've been in Dacca myself – back in sixty-six,' he said, surprised. 'I was there for nearly five months. Where were you staying?'

'In Dhanmandi . . . Seventeenth street. Not far from the Nepalese Embassy. And you?'

'I stayed with some local friends near the new mosque and the bazaar. It's really a pity we didn't meet before.'

'Even so, it's a small world, isn't it?' said Alister.

After the Civil War, when East Pakistan became the People's Republic of Bangladesh and left the British Commonwealth, the couple left the country, first for India, where they spent nearly five years doing pharmaceutical research; then to Pakistan, where they lived in Karachi, in Lahore. 'We liked Bangladesh best, but not all that "People's Republic" stuff,' Alister explained. 'Nor the idea of living outside the Commonwealth . . . I think Mujibar Rahman made a great mistake when he decided to sever all British ties, just when his country needed them most . . . But the Orientals always swing from one extreme to the other.'

Alister and Natalie had been in Peshawar on a few weeks' holiday, before moving to Australia, when the Soviet troops invaded Afghanistan. 'We decided to stay and help the refugees.' Natalie concluded. 'We just couldn't remain indifferent to so much suffering.'

Alister and Natalie did what other sensible foreigners were doing: they tried to help the wretched refugees the way they could. Natalie carried all the clothes, bedding and foodstuff she could spare into the nearest camp. Dipping into their joint account, Alister purchased nearly five-hundred pounds worth of food and medicines – a drop in the ocean, as they knew, but nevertheless of some help. In the end they 'adopted' four children, two boys and two girls, none older than six, to take care of them until things got better.

Not long afterwards Alister and Natalie ran across some guerrillas who had come to Peshawar to buy weapons and ammunition, and eventually they met Haydar Chari, already a famous *mojahedin* whose guerrillas kept the escape routes to Pakistan open. From Haydar's grim account of events, incredible stories emerged, of individual heroism and self-sacrifice, making it quite clear how the freedom fighters were utterly determined to overthrow the Soviets, no matter how tremendous the odds. It was still the very beginning of the resistance. Terrified and hesitant at first, the *mojahedins* soon hit back, learned the enemy's weakness and became bolder. Practice yielded experience and skill: the once-green volunteers became veteran experts, capable of dealing with tanks, artillery and infantry. Only the jet fighter-bombers and helicopter gunships remained beyond reach. The *mojahedins* had no weapon against the Russian Air Force.

'Those wretched copters,' Haydar Chari kept saying one evening, over a cup of tea. 'We've got to find a way to defend ourselves against them. The Egyptians and the Chinese are sending us rockets, but it takes ages and there are only a few, anyway. And in the meantime the Russian planes roam the hills and destroy our villages at leisure. Sometimes the copters descend to thirty feet above the ground and the crew sit back and laugh, and use the people running away as target practice for their pistols.'

Alister had been sitting for a while in thoughtful

silence. Now he glanced up and said quietly; 'Perhaps we could offer you a temporary solution – although only on a very limited scale.'

Haydar Chari's chin came up. 'Something against the copters?' he asked eagerly.

Alister nodded. 'That's right.'

'What?'

'A small guerrilla air force,' Alister replied with a smile while Chari stared at him, baffled. 'I'm not joking,' Alister added reassuringly. He went to the next room and returned with a two-foot model of a wartime Spitfire, with a small petrol engine. He placed it lovingly on the table. 'Remote control,' he explained. 'It may be hard to believe, but this little chap can fly eighty miles an hour – even faster in a dive, and perform like a real plane.'

Haydar Chari still couldn't quite understand what Alister had in mind. 'But what can it do against an enemy copter?' he asked.

'Quite a lot, if we load it with explosive,' Alister answered. 'It can carry more than you can pack in a hand-grenade.'

A brief, astonished silence ensued. Staring at the toy, Haydar Chari pondered over the incredible proposition. Then his eyes became intense. 'Do you mean – it could actually be guided to hit a Russian helicopter?'

Alister nodded. 'To tell you the truth I can't see how any copter could get away from it.'

Haydar Chari gasped. 'But, then . . . this is something . . . very great . . . '

'Also very expensive, Haydar,' Alister said rather pointedly. 'This little model cost us nearly three hundred pounds.'

Chari shook his head. 'Three hundred pounds is not much for a Russian gunship,' he said with a grin.

'Well, it's quite a lot to us,' Natalie teased.

'Money is no problem,' Haydar said evenly. 'We are not rich, but our people are prepared to make sacrifices. We have gold and silver, also some jade . . . ' He picked up the model plane and studied it from every angle. Then, glancing up, he asked, 'Can you show me how it works?'

'Certainly.'

Alister beckoned him into the garden where he demonstrated the Spitfire in flight, drawing a crowd of spectators round the garden wall. The small fighter rose quite high and performed sharp turns and loops, rolled like a real plane, and dived at great speed before landing smoothly on the path.

Haydar Chari was deeply impressed. 'I think you're right – it *is* too agile for any copter to get away from it! Will it be possible for you to build more?'

'Only two – we haven't got any engines.'

'Or parts for the remote control.' Natalie added.

'Where can you buy them?'

'In Europe or Japan,' said Alister. 'Or Hongkong . . . But there'd be the problem of Pakistani Customs.'

Haydar waved an airy hand. 'Pakistani Customs is only a matter of a little baksheesh . . . I'm going to talk to some important people. We'll give you the money for all the expenses. This idea of your could change the whole course of the war in Afghanistan. Without their copters the Russians would be lost in the mountains. They don't like the idea of parachuting into our wilderness, unless they have copters standing by to rescue them if the strike misfires.'

'I can well believe that,' Alister agreed. 'Well, if your people can come up with the money, we're quite willing to help you. Unfortunately we aren't rich enough to pay for it ourselves, otherwise, we'd do it gladly.'

Haydar Chari left soon afterwards, and Alister and Natalie began experimenting with explosives and primers, using simple gliders for testing the various systems. None was wholly satisfactory. In the end, a Canadian zoologist working in Pakistan solved the problem: he showed Alister the tiny detonator that propelled the rubber plunger of the Cap-Chur syringe, used for immobilising wild animals. The American detonator was light, sensitive and absolutely reliable. During the tests it exploded at the slightest impact to set off an ordinary shotgun shell, which in turn ignoted the three-ounce gelignite charge which the model carried. Launched from a low hill, the test glider flew a hundred yards into an abandoned lorry, exploded on impact and blew a thirty-inch chunk from the chassis.

'Well, I imagine that could have brought down any copter,' Alister said happily, while the idea occurred to him that a larger model with a ten c.c. engine would be able to carry enough explosive to damage a tank. He was certain that their remote-controlled 'flying bombs' as the Afghans called the model aircraft, would be a most serious threat to Soviet copters, lorries and fuel tankers. He felt strangely elated – not simply because he was anti-Russian, but because he was able to give something to the vulnerable freedom fighters with which to defend themselves against the ruthless aggressor.

Abdi Jubal, a young *mojahedin* motor mechanic, whom Haydar Chari had left behind to give a hand with the testing, asked eagerly: 'How far can a model like this fly?'

'It depends on the capacity of the fuel tank and the range of the wireless control,' Alister replied. 'But several miles, any way.'

Jubal's face lit up. 'But then we could even attack the stationary enemy fighter-bombers on their bases. Mr Alister, your invention might save Afghanistan!'

'Don't get too excited, Jubal. The Soviets can send in more planes than we can possibly destroy . . . But we can certainly give them a run for their money.'

The successful tests marked the birth of the guerrilla 'air force' of three small model planes, each with the destructive power of a hand-grenade.

Haydar Chari returned with six young men who spoke reasonable English and were to be the first 'pilots' of the *mojahedin* 'air force'. He also brought along a bag of gold coins for Alister to convert into hard cash, financing the venture. (It never occurred to him to ask for a receipt. He considered the Englishman a genuine friend who wanted to help the hard-pressed Afghans.) Alister flew off to Karachi and thence to Japan, probably the cheapest source of parts; Natalie, herself a modelling expert, began training Haydar Chari's 'airmen' – all former engineering students in Kabul, to assemble and 'fly' the models.

Alister returned ten days later and had a lively exchange with the head of Customs at the airport who, after studying the invoices, remarked with a serene smile that it must be nice to have enough money to pursue such an expensive hobby. But while his assistants busied themselves with the amount of duty payable on the imported parts, he invited Alister into his office for a cup of tea. The duty came to nearly four hundred pounds, but when Hassan Khan learned of the true nature of Alister's 'hobby' he broke into hearty laughter and said appreciatively; 'Well, well, sir – that's an entirely different matter. We ought to do our best to help the Afghans – it could be us tomorrow.'

Reclassified as cheap toys, the duty came down to fifty pounds and the guerrilla 'air force' was safely on its way to Peshawar.

Alister brought back enough parts to build twenty-four models, some with engines powerful enough to allow for a larger load of explosive. With the help of the engineering students, the models were assembled, then test-flown without detonators in case minor adjustments were needed. The planes were different, but all performed perfectly, including a twin-engine, 1940-vintage B-25 Mitchell bomber which carried a pound of explosive.

Accompanied by Haydar Chari and twenty *mojahedins* Alister and Natalie embarked for the Mommands to initiate and supervise the first actions of the guerrilla 'air force'.

It was the eleventh Russian attack on the suspected camp of Haydar Chari in the Mommands; once again, it was a mile or so off target, for the crafty local rebels had not one but six encampments in the region, though only one of them was actually in use at any given time.

First came a flight of six MiGs, screaming over the plateau: Pulling up sharply before the snow-capped cliffs they rolled into elongated turns, to repeat their strafing runs from the other direction, while a squadron of copters, two of them heavy, twin-rotor transports, approached warily, preparing to land. None of the *mojahedins* stirred. So far the enemy were ignorant of their exact positions. Why alert them while they were still out of range?

Out of range for rifles and machine guns, but not for Alister and Natalie's 'flying bombs'.

She turned on the engine and adjusted the fuel. Alister tested the remote control and moved the rudder and the elevators, feeling genuinely sorry for the little Spitfire. He wished it were a Messerschmitt, or a Japanese Zero, and the idea kept nagging at him to try and build models which could fire small explosive projectiles and then return home, instead of destroying themselves. Making a mental note on the subject, Alister decided he must discuss it with some expert gunmakers in Peshawar. If the model aircrafts could fire, destroy and return intact, the guerrilla 'air force' would indeed became very effective.

The hoarse voice of Haydar Chari brought him back to earth. 'Try and get the large copter. It's probably loaded with troops.'

The twin-rotor craft was barely six hundred yards from where they sheltered. Natalie lifted the Spitfire, turned on the engine and held it into the breeze.

'I'm ready.'

'Let her go!'

She swung the model out over the ravine. It sank a few feet, then started to climb at an amazing rate and turned towards the Soviet aircraft. Almost awestruck, the *mojahedins* followed the flight of the 'flying bomb' as it rose from the ravine, levelled off at the altitude of the copter and streaked towards it. The distance narrowed.

250 yards . . . 200 yards . . .

Natalie was chewing her lip. Haydar wiped his sweating forehead.

'They saw it!' yelled a man called Abdul Karay, and sprang onto a slab of rock to get a better view. Alister noticed himself that the heavy copter was turning and rising, but the little Spitfire shot after it, levelled out again and smashed into the cockpit.

Holding their breath, the spectators did not hear the explosion which was drowned by the clatter of the rotors, but they saw the flash, and the smoke blowing from the cockpit. The huge copter dropped on its side and went down at a crazy angle, distintegrating on the rock-strewn slope, pieces of fuselage, bodies, crates and a pair of field guns – everything went tumbling back into the steep ravine.

'Allah!' Haydar Chari cried. 'The sparrows killed the eagle!'

Around them the *mojahedins* broke into wild cheers, but the successful event had an even happier aftermath.

'There is another one!' Abdul Karay shouted, pointing to the scene of the crash. Probably unaware of the true cause of the disaster, a gunship was circling the wreckage preparing to land. Haydar grabbed Alister's arm. 'If you get that one too, they will probably leave the Mommands for good.'

Alister glance at his wife. 'What do you think?'

She shrugged. 'We might be heading for a lot of trouble with our aerobatics.' But she started up the second model, a miniature facsimile of the American Hellcat. She shrugged again and gave a sigh.

'Here we go . . .'

It was easy. The gunship had already landed and Alister guided it straight into the rotor cowling. The blast wrecked the transmission. The engine died and the blades stopped. The crew ran for shelter.

After this second mishap the rest of the copters clattered away, but the jets went berserk. Streaking over the hillside, they rocketed, bombed and strafed the barren slopes and the plateau, six hundred yards from where the happy band watched the Soviet merry-go-round.

'Would it be possible to hit one of the MiGs?' Haydar Chari asked eagerly and Alister shook his head. 'I don't think so. They're too fast.' Then he added reassuringly, 'But we can build model jets later on.'

'Try it,' Haydar gloated. 'Try it by all means.'

Alister slapped him on the back. 'In the meantime, we'll try to build something for you to attack the fighter-bombers parked on their airfields.'

With the MiGs buzzing like angry bees and doing low-level aerobatics over the rugged terrain, another helicopter made a

161

spirited attempt to rescue three stranded comrades from an overhang. Natalie launched the third model, but, probably alert by now, the Russians spotted it, fired a few useless bursts, then took off at great speed and escaped. Alister brought back the second Hellcat and tried to land it on a relatively smooth stretch of flat, but it blew up anyway on touch-down: the detonator was too sensitive. It was an annoying loss.

The stranded Russians were hunted down by Haydar's men.

The Red Air Force departed, leaving behind two smouldering wrecks and twenty-two corpses.

The news of the 'flying bombs' spread like wildfire through the Mommands and Alister and Natalie were not sure if they liked their overnight popularity. But the guerrilla 'air force' was becoming a genuine terror for Soviet copter crews, who had no idea how to defend themselves against the small, speedy monsters. In most instances, by the time the models were spotted it was already too late to escape.

Changing camp every few days, staying in nearly inaccessible caves, Alister and Natalie spent six weeks in the Mommands assembling explosive model airplanes, training more *mojahedins* to make and fly them.

Fired with enthusiam and growing bolder, the 'pilots' of Haydar Chari embarked on more ambitious ventures, including a daring 'air-raid' on a dozen stationary MiGs near Jalalabad. A squadron of three models, guided from a forested slope almost two miles away, hit a pair of fighters which caught fire and ingited three more planes and a petrol tanker. The conflagration spread quickly and the final balance of the raid comprised twelve MiGs, the tanker and three towing vehicles.

When Jim and engineer Gawar arrived in the Mommands Alister and Natalie were about to leave. From talkative villagers, or perhaps from tortured prisoners or paid informers, the Karmalists had eventually learned about the couple and their 'flying bombs' which had virtually stopped

Russian copter activity in the important border region.

The Soviet High Command considered the explosive models a serious threat and the Afghan authorities offered a very large reward for the delivery of the 'dangerous imperialist agents', who were 'backed by the CIA'.

One hundred and fifty thousand Afghani was approximately two thousand pounds; a real fortune in poverty-stricken Afghanistan.

'Sooner or later someone's going to sell us lock, stock and barrel,' Alister told Jim, who agreed.

'You'd better base your aircraft industry in Pakistan,' he told the couple, 'and not too close to the border, either.'

The next day the Russian Air Force subjected the suspected area to heavy bombing and napalm attacks, after which a battalion of paratroopers landed barely four miles from Haydar's improvised camp. A vicious battle ensued in which the better-equipped Russians gradually gained ground. After losing fifty men, Haydar Chari broke contact and withdrew; he neatly evacuated his camp, and moved into higher, more easily defended ground. The enemy occupied the empty camp, but lost two more copters to the 'flying bombs' which Alister and Natalie guided down from a safe outcrop nearly two thousand feet above.

It was their last battle action in Afghanistan. The same evening, making a twenty-mile detour, a group of *mojahedins* escorted the British couple to Pashat, and then across the border to Nawangai in Pakistan.

Alister and Natalie returned to Peshawar where, lacking engines for the moment, they constructed ten radio-controlled gliders, each with a six-foot wingspan and one-and-a-half pound explosive packed in the fuselage.

Jim and engineer Gawar took the godforsaken trails back to the Khawak. Carefully packed in padded crates were eight powered 'flying bombs' and the parts for six gliders. Two of Haydar's 'pilots' came along to train Ghazi's would-be experts.

The record of the *mojahedin* 'air force' was impressive. Of the first series of models assembled by Alister and Natalie, eleven succeeded in wrecking flying, or stationary copters and fighters. A pair of 'flying bombs' hit the staff car of the Soviet Commander of Jalalabad, and an Afghan Army truck transporting mortar shells. Three planes had missed targets and blew themselves up.

The silent gliders were used against enemy ground installations and vehicle parks with great success and to the dismay of the Russians, who found themselves wholly defenceless against the silent menace, launched against them during the twilight hours from hills, attics or minarets. The gliders penetrated the most heavily defended areas and caused considerable losses in lives and materials.

Ali Ghazi's 'air force' played havoc at Charikar and on the Soviet airbase at Bagram. The gliders soared in from the darkness to demolish stationary helicopters, MiGs, stacks of oil drums, lorries and magazines. One glider crashed into the office of a Soviet general; another into the officer's housing complex, a third 'flying bomb' decimated a lorry load of soldiers. It was a bit like the German V-1 blitz over London, except that the German missiles were bulky enough to be spotted and fired at, and made a lot of noise. The gliders gave no warning.

Daring to fly over the Khawak region, the Soviet Air Force lost eight more gunships and two twin-rotor transports to Ali Ghazi's powered models and the Chinese rapid-fire gun.

Then Haydar Chari learned of a Karmalist plot to send a four-man commando, posing as *mojahedins* to Peshawar with orders to seek out and eliminate the 'imperialist agents'. Wasting no time, he sent a pair of riders to warn Alister and Natalie. Taking the important components and twenty newly-arrived engines, the couple moved to Rawalpindi, together with their four little refugee wards; while the guerrillas of Haydar and a few local Pathan friends settled down in the vacant house to give the Karmalist commando its deserved reception. But the anticipated raid never materialised. The assigned killers had either lost heart, or changed sides and defected to Pakistan as bona-fide refugees. Or else the whole thing had been a groundless rumour.

Before leaving Pakistan, Alister and Natalie had built some seventy 'flying bombs', forty of them powered, the rest gliders. The workshop of Dahi Baba manufactured eighteen more – until Pakistani Customs unexpectedly clamped down on the import of parts, without offering any official explanation.

'Someone at the Soviet Embassy in Islamabad must have been complaining,' Jim commented and Ali Ghazi agreed. The arms of the Kremlin were long – although not long enough to squeeze China.

Placed under heavy pressure by the Soviets and the Afghan Army, Haydar Chari decided to abandon the Mommands, at least for the time being, and join forces in the Khawak with Ali Ghazi, who occupied a virtually impregnable position in the Anjuman range and whose *mojahedins* had already repulsed several enemy offensives. Needless to say, Ali Ghazi gladly accommodated Haydar and his four hundred men. Their united force of over a thousand well-equipped fighters controlled four roads, including the main Kabul-USSR road, and were within striking distance of the capital. They were also fairly well coordinated with Acar Yarim's group in the Hindukush, and with Safed Yar in the Koh-i-Baba range, north of the Irak pass – forming an invisible guerrilla ring which encircled Kabul and the enemy bases around it. The enemy could use the main road, but not without danger. In order to send supply lorries from Kabul to Ghazni, or to Haibak, the invaders were forced to use armoured cars and troop carriers with gunships flying overhead. 'A costly way of transporting goods,' as Ali Ghazi put it. And when, despite all precautions, the *mojahedins* managed to knock out a few armoured cars or copters, the 'cost of transporting' became more than the value of the 'goods'.

No Soviet or Karmalist vehicle would dare to use any road at night – unless the occupants were deserters. The guerrillas therefore would seldom attack a solitary enemy vehicle moving at night, especially with its turret guns reversed. They would stop peacefully at the first challenge.

The 'council of war' in the Anjuman now consisted of Ali Ghazi, Haydar Chari, Ahmad Mazar, Captain Karatash, Musa Gawar and Acar Yarim. 'Honorary members' were Safak Parakin and Jim – despite his repeated protestations that he was about to leave Afghanistan for Karachi and 'good old England'. The last time he said that, the *mojahedins* rewarded him with cheerful pandemonium and Ahmad Mazar boomed: 'Come, come, my infidel friend, you're not leaving us *again*?'

'This time I'm deadly serious,' said Jim, trying to keep a straight face.

Ali Ghazi shook his head and said reprovingly; 'You want to leave us now? Just when we're planning to reorganise our 'air force' on an even larger scale?'

'What do you mean, Ali?'

'I mean – someone's got to go to Hongkong, Jim, to get the components . . . '

'And that someone should be me.'

'Hongkong is a British colony . . . it would be easy for you, Jim . . . Not for us. Visa problems and all that.'

'Yes – all that . . . And what if I scarper?'

'You'd never do that. We're brothers, are we not?'

'Damn you, anyway, how would you bring the parts into Afghanistan?'

'Zebak Vahan is already organising that in Sinkiang.'

Jim groaned. 'Just don't ask me to ride back here all the way from Hongkong.'

RED SNOW

Gently sloping down to Dwatoi in Pakistan, one of the foot-hills of the Safed Koh range ran ruby red, like a summer pasture strewn with poppies. But it was mid-winter, the undulating land lay under snow and the ruby-red flowers were frozen patches of blood. Four hundred fugitives and pack animals can spill a great deal of blood. To the inspecting Soviet staff officers and Karmalist Government officials the landscape must have presented a truly enchanting sight.

Eighty *mojahedins*, escorting a caravan of refugees to Pakistan, had also died. They had been blocked, encircled and slaughtered by Russian paratroopers and Afghan Army commandos who had dropped in to their midst wearing breathing apparatus, while squadrons of copters showered canisters of heavy yellow tear gas into the field. The gas incapacitated men and beasts and killed elderly people and young children within minutes. A company of Karmalist infantry cut off the way of escape towards the border, only two miles away, and the handicapped *mojahedins* could not even fire at the enemy without hitting each other, or the panicking refugees with whom the paratroopers shielded themselves.

It was a debacle; a truly apocalyptic scene, with people tottering blindly, mown down by bullets, or collapsing, gasping for air. Screaming mothers staggered in knee-deep snow, trying to shelter their babies, already suffo-cated themselves, falling in coughing fits and spitting blood, while the masked paratroopers poured bullets into whoever was still moving, regardless of age and sex. The few who had managed to flee from the gas were hunted down by the roving gunships. Only some sixteen had managed to reach Dwatoi.

The bodies were left where they had fallen. Wolves, vultures and hyenas converged from far and wide for the feast. Well-fed and bold, the carrion-eaters had never had it so good until the arrival of the Red Army. They lay in wait until the massacre was over, then advanced in small packs to feed. No one disturbed them. The Russians hunted for men, not beasts; they, too, lay in wait, hoping to ambush the bereaved relatives, should they return to gather their dead. But, grief-stricken as they were, the survivors knew better. No one returned.

Of the victims' luggage only worn clothes, old bedding and worthless cutlery remained. Everything of value – money, jewellery, prayer rugs, carpets and kelims – had been looted by the Russians and the Karmalists.

Legitimate spoils of war.

When a ring or bracelet could not be removed, the finger or arm would be hacked off.

Thousands of miles away the noble and dignified delegates of the United Nations gathered in their great assembly hall to debate Israel's occupation of the Golan Heights.

Sixty miles to the north, in the province of Askhun, a Soviet helicopter gunship bearing the serial number 1317, had machine-gunned and rocketed the village of Pashat near the border; afterwards, it had to make an emergency landing. Before their rescue party arrived, the enraged villagers stormed the copter; they lost forty of their own men, but they lynched the crew and set fire to the machine. MiGs bombed the area. Copter-borne Afghan infantry landed. Under the command of Soviet officers, they ransacked every house still standing, and summarily executed every male inhabitant over four-foot-ten.

But the invaders and the Karmalist traitors did not always have it easy. All their 'successful' operations were viciously retaliated for by the *mojahedins,* whose ranks constantly swelled, despite their losses, as more and more embittered men took to the mountains. When they weren't driven by patriotism or religious fervour they joined the guerrillas simply to seek revenge for dead relatives.

Then and there, captured Russians would be lynched, or –

at best – shot. Captured Karmalists were no longer merely disarmed and released, but beaten, abused and often hanged. Babrak Karmal's Moscow-trained agitators, the Communist cadres of the 'Parcham' Party, received no mercy anywhere. They were treated as traitors to their country, to Allah and Islam and hanged, or stoned to death.

The majority of Party activists were university students from Kabul. As in the free world, students rebel by nature against *any* existing order, and they made receptive recruits for the Marxist-Leninist ideology, which apparently endowed them with power to overthrow the 'old' and establish the 'new' system. A system which promised them more 'freedom' and less discipline.

The life of a politically active student in a Communist society is easy. He does not have to study hard to earn honours. His Party membership, or well-positioned relatives will always ensure his success. A non-Communist professor who failed a Communist student would quickly vanish from the board of lecturers.

Karmal's agitators dispersed in the villages to spread Marxist-Leninist slogans – and died by the dozen. The *mojahedins* had no feelings for them at all.

If they were singled out and caught, they died.

Safed Yar's guerrillas ambushed a Russian container-convoy fifty miles south of Doshi. The *mojahedins* had dumped a mixture of petrol, oil and ground charcoal on to a five-hundred-yard section of the road, and when the enemy lorries rolled into the sticky stuff they set fire to it. The drivers tried to speed out of the inferno, but the faster they rolled the more flaming matter was splashed on to the undercarriage and the vehicles behind. In the end, drivers and escort abandoned the convoy, fled into the fields and perished in the guerrilla crossfire. Forty-two lorries and a large number of enemy troops were bagged by Safed Yar that night. The guerrillas did not suffer a single casualty.

The attack was well timed. Already familiar with the Russian ways, Yar limited the action to twelve minutes, slightly less than was necessary for the Soviet MiGs to reach the scene. By the time the fighter planes arrived, the *mojahedins* were safely in the hills – and to Safed Yar's delight, the strafing fighters mistook the fleeing Russians and Afghan Army infantry for 'rebels' and subjected them to rocket and machine-gun fire for several minutes.

Mobile rocket launchers, mortars and heavy armaments began to arrive from friendly nations, mostly from China, broadening the scope of guerrilla activity. Heavily guarded Soviet bases were now vulnerable. Enemy housing complexes were attacked. The cadres of Babrak Karmal died by the score. High-ranking officers, police chiefs, local administrators, government functionaries, and 'Parcham' Party agitators became free-for-all targets. None of them dared show himself in public and the locations of their residences were kept secret. But sooner or later the *mojahedins* discovered the hated collaborators, and when they could not kill them, they exterminated their families. Karmalist policemen who served as torturers and jailers in prisons were marked men, with an average life-expectancy of six months.

Desperate to please his Soviet backers, Babrak Karmal spent his wrath on the 'rebel' villages. Since neither the Afghan Army nor the Russians could hold any territory lying further than a dozen miles from the main highways, Karmal satisfied himself with rapid, devastating raids on the rural communities. These attacks on the villages were senseless acts of brutality: the *mojahedins* would never establish themselves in any exposed locality, as the 'government' well knew. Nevertheless, the slaughtering of the rural population continued until many villages were virtually deserted.

The idea was that the guerrillas would be unable to survive in a desert, without food or shelter.

Acar Yarim had built himself a quite fearsome reputation and in the end the Karmalist troops would rather desert, than go into action in the Hindukush mountains.

Yarim had caught a mixed group of Soviet paratroops and Karmalist infantry trying to seize the Baigakh Pass. The fierce guerrilla leader had the prisoners' throats cut, collected the blood in barrels, then laid out the corpses on an open field in the form of the Communist star and had the words spelled out in the snow with blood: 'Welcome to the Baigakh', for the copters to orient themselves.

Yarim had also captured six light howitzers in action. The *mojahedins* hauled them to the highway near Doshi and shelled the Russian base until the ammunition ran out. Destroying the useless artillery, leaving behind five burning barracks and a dozen wrecked lorries and tankers, Yarim retreated into the wilderness. The next morning the Karmalists raided the village of Kinjan, arrested twenty men and shot them in a snowfield. Five days later, the guerrillas of Acar Yarim stole into Doshi and blew up the residence of the Afghan Army commander responsible for the Kinjan executions. The colonel was away, but his wife and children died, together with the six soldiers guarding the house.

Haydar Chari and three hundred of his men descended from the Khawak and wiped out the four-hundred-strong Afghan Army garrison and its fifteen Soviet 'advisers' at Silala. Six Soviet officers escaped by copter. Three others were caught trying to flee Lalpura in a staff car. Haydar Chari had them hanged. Frozen solid, the corpses hung for ten days before a copter recovered them, while low-flying MiGs patrolled the neighbourhood.

One of Alister and Natalie's 'flying bombs' guided by engineer Musa Gawar, brought down an Afghan Air Force copter with a major-general and two staff officers on an inspection tour. Secret papers salvaged from the wreck enabled Ali Ghazi to annihilate a battalion of Karmalists in the Panjshir valley.

Posing as irrigation project workers, the guerrillas of Haydar Chari executed a brilliant raid against the police headquarters of Jalalabad. They freed fourteen prisoners and seized a list of secret police collaborators working for the Karmal regime. Twenty-eight traitors from neighbouring villages, most of them teachers and students, and even one *mullah* were searched out, lured into traps and executed by the *mojahedins*. The action cleared the Jalalabad-Lalpura-

Chiga Sarai triangle of Karmalist informers for many months.

The Russians bombed and shelled villages, strafed mountain trails and decimated refugee caravans: but increasingly they refrained from sending infantry into the mountains. Troops sent into the mountains seldom returned. The snow in the mountains ran red.

EPILOGUE

OVER TWO years have passed since the events of this brief record of Afghan heroism. Haydar Chari and Acar Yarim have died in action, but their determined followers have fought on, under the leadership of Ali Ghazi Khan. Together with Safed Yar he has become the undisputed, if not uncontested, master of some 18,000 square miles of rugged land, in the centre of which, like beleaguered, occupied islands lie four important cities: Kabul, Charikar, Seh Baba and Jalalabad, with nearly half the enemy forces confined to the bases near the capital and the vital main roads. But the *mojahedins* have turned the highways into 'toll-roads' – and the enemy pays to use them in blood.

Nowadays the freedom fighters of Afghanistan are faring better. They are also better organised and more united. Having smoothed over their personal, ideological and religious differences, reputable national resistance leaders emerged and joined forces. The Islamic Alliance of the Afghan Mojahedin came into being.

Having realised that Afghan resistance did not crumble 'within a few months' – as had been predicted – the free world is now sending help. But that 'great forum of humanity', the United Nations, is still silent and shuns the very idea of criticising, let alone putting sanctions on the USSR. It is safer to chastise the South American military juntas, Israel and South Africa: in the free press, the slaughter of fifty civilians in Central America makes headlines. Five thousand bombed, machine-gunned and executed in Afghanistan gets a few paragraphs on the back page. The unpredictable Russian bear must be left alone.

The free world should be glad that the Red Army has not yet moved into Pakistan, or Iran, or Poland.

Who would oppose it?

The snow on the hills and mountains of Afghanistan runs red. It will be running red for many years – until the Kremlin sends a million troops, stations a regiment in every village, a tank every five hundred yards of every road and a helicopter gunship on every peak.

But the winter of the Afghan highlands is no more benevolent than 'General Winter' who halted and destroyed the German invaders before they reached Moscow and Leningrad; and the freedom fighters in the Afghan mountains are no less embittered and determined than the partisans of the Ukraine and Bielorussia were in their day.

Those who fight for their homeland and their freedom can do wonders and can never be defeated. The Soviet leadership should know that better than anyone. All the Red Army will ever hold in Afghanistan is *Kizilkar* . . . Red Snow.

GLOSSARY

R: Russian   P: Pushto

Agon (R)	Fire!
Allah akhbar (P)	God is great!
Atiec (R)	Father
Baba (P)	Father
Csto palamales? (R)	What is the damage?
Csto sluchilas? (R)	What happened?
Da (R)	Yes
Davai (R)	Move; Forward
Dochka (R)	Little girl
Dolgoli vozniot pochenitz? (R)	How long does it take?
Gospodin (R)	Sir
Haraso (R)	Okay
Idi, idite (R)	Come: Go
Insallah (P)	As God wills it
Kalachnikov	Soviet automatic rifle
Karmalist	Follower of Babrak Karmal
Masallah (P)	Expression of satisfaction
Matka (R)	Mother
Nepriateli (R)	Enemy
Nichevo vaznogo (R)	Nothing serious
Nie strillay (R)	Don't shoot!
Niekrich (R)	Shut up!
Niet (R)	No
Ochin haraso (R)	Very well; Very good
Paidom (R)	Let's go
Palkovnik (R)	Colonel
Partizanski (R)	Guerrilla
Pol chesa (R)	Half an hour
Rimien (R)	Chain; Tracks
Samaliotchik (R)	Airman
Sestra (R)	Sister
Slushai (R)	Listen
Spakoini nochi	Good-night
Starshina (R)	Sergeant
Suda (R)	Here
Te Svolech (R)	You s.o.b.
Tovarich (R)	Comrade
Vrach (R)	Physician
Ya som (R)	I am

NEL BESTSELLERS

SURVIVALIST 1: TOTAL WAR   *Jerry Ahern* £1.50
SURVIVALIST 2: THE NIGHTMARE BEGINS   *Jerry Ahern* £1.50
SURVIVALIST 3: THE QUEST   *Jerry Ahern* £1.50
THE MOSCOW OPTION   *David Downing* £1.25
DEVIL'S GUARD   *George Elford* £1.95
I BOUGHT A STAR   *Thomas Firbank* £0.90
WORLD WAR III   *Brian Harris* £1.25
ASSAULT TROOP 1: BLOOD BEACH   *Ian Harding* £1.50
ASSAULT TROOP 2: DEATH IN THE FOREST   *Ian Harding* £1.50
ASSAULT TROOP 3: CLASH ON THE RHINE   *Ian Harding* £1.60
LOS CHICOS DE LA GUERRA   *Daniel Kon* £2.95
PQ17 CONVOY TO HELL   *Lund & Ludlam* £0.75
THE WAR OF THE LANDING CRAFT   *Lund & Ludlam* £0.80
JERSEY UNDER THE JACKBOOT   *R. C. F. Maugham, C.B.E.* £0.95
DIEPPE: THE DAWN OF DECISION   *Jacques Mordal* £1.75
GATEWAY TO HELL   *James Rouch* £0.95
TIGER   *James Rouch* £1.25
THE WAR MACHINES   *James Rouch* £1.25
THE ZONE 1: HARD TARGET   *James Rouch* £1.00
THE ZONE 2: BLIND FIRE   *James Rouch* £1.00
THE ZONE 4: SKY STRIKE   *James Rouch* £1.25
THE ZONE 5: OVERKILL   *James Rouch* £1.25
THE LAST BATTLE   *Cornelius Ryan* £2.95
THE LONGEST DAY   *Cornelius Ryan* £1.95

All these books are available at your local bookshop or newsagent, or can be ordered direct from the publisher. Just tick the titles you want and fill in the form below.

NEL P.O. BOX 11, FALMOUTH TR10 9EN, CORNWALL

Postage Charge:

U.K. Customers 45p for the first book plus 20p for the second book and 14p for each additional book ordered to a maximum charge of £1.63.

B.F.P.O. & EIRE Customers 45p for the first book plus 20p for the second book and 14p for the next 7 books; thereafter 8p per book.

Overseas Customers 75p for the first book and 21p per copy for each additional book.

Please send cheque or postal order (no currency).

Name ....

Address ....

....

Title ....

While every effort is made to keep prices steady, it is sometimes necessary to increase prices at short notice. New English Library reserve the right to show on covers and charge new retail prices which may differ from those advertised in the text or elsewhere.